(

Our Family and IT

Rachel Fearnley

© Rachel Fearnley, 2018

Published by Olop and Flossie Publishing

A CIP catalogue record for this book is available from the British Library.

ISBN 978-1-9996838-0-1

Book layout and design by Clare Brayshaw

Cover design by Stuart Trotter

Prepared and printed by:

York Publishing Services Ltd
64 Hallfield Road
Layerthorpe
York YO31 7ZQ

Tel: 01904 431213

Website: www.yps-publishing.co.uk

To Barry, with all my love.

Acknowledgments

There are many people, who without their support and encouragement this book would not have happened. Thank you to Margaret and Graham Rippon for encouraging me to believe that I had a story to tell.

Thank you to Liz Mills, Dr Carole Comben, Shirley Quinn, Olly Clabburn and Margaret Rippon for proof reading and commenting on the book. I am indebted to you for generously giving your time to share your thoughts and for your encouragement.

A special thank you to Duncan Beal and the brilliant team at York Publishing Company, especially Clare Brayshaw. Duncan's knowledge and experience of book publishing has been invaluable in supporting a novice like me.

Thanks to Barrie Cresswell for the technical advice and support.

Thank you to Amy Thompson and Luke France for sharing your knowledge and practice. Your advice helped add credibility to an important chapter.

Thank you to Dr David Booton for generously sharing your expert knowledge. I am very grateful.

Thank you to my family and friends who have harnessed the power of social media to help me promote the book, especially to Charlotte Pinder my TN.

And finally thank you to Barry. Thank you for all your support, encouragement and belief in my work. Thank you for planting the idea for the book and for having the foresight to see that this alternative route to getting my message out there could be the answer. Thank you for sharing the journey with me and for being there. As always without your support I would not have been able to do this.

About the author

Our Family and IT is Rachel's debut novel. Rachel has worked in social care for many years as a practitioner, researcher and campaigner. Rachel's primary area of academic interest is the impact of parental life-limiting illness on children and family life. Rachel has previously written academic books and papers on this subject.

ONE

Rebecca

I turned and gave Granny one more wave before our car went round the corner. I could see her standing in the middle of the road waving, her red and white checked apron round her waist and her bright yellow cardigan buttoned up against the cold winter wind. I knew she was crying even though she was pretending she wasn't. She always cried when we set off home after our holidays with her.

TWO

Angela

Driving home following a stay with Mum was always tinged with sadness but as we left after our Christmas break I felt an additional wrench. It had been a lovely few days. The children all appeared to have had a good time and Nathan and I had also had time to relax. Just being with Mum was always special for me; I didn't see her as often as I would have liked and although we spoke at least twice a week on the telephone it wasn't quite the same. I hugged Mum one last time before we set off, told her I loved her and that it wouldn't be long before we saw her again.

We all gave the sea one last wave as the car turned inland and we lost the coast road. I sat back in the car watching the tree-lined road flash by as the miles were swiftly swept away. The darkness of the trees was foreboding, a brooding menace that I had not really noticed before. Maybe it was because we were later setting off from Mum's than usual and the winter sunshine was quickly giving way to the low glow of twilight.

I thought back about the week with Mum. As always there had been much anticipation about our stay and great excitement when we arrived. Mum had bustled round us all making sure we were fed after the long drive to her house. The cottage was as warm and cosy as I always remembered it to be. Mum had lit the fire and the warmth was a lovely welcome home when we arrived. The normally tidy, formal 'best room' quickly lost its identity as the children unceremoniously dumped all their belongings in there and all the Christmas presents were stashed under the tree.

Mum was always at her happiest when we went to stay and especially at Christmas. She was able to indulge in her passion for baking. Since Dad had died she didn't get many opportunities to do this so when we visited she went on a great baking spree and tried hard to make our time with her as special as possible.

A Christmassy mix of smells had greeted us as we walked into the house. The log fire gently letting off its earthy smell that epitomised my childhood home. The fir tree in the corner standing proud, decorated with a mixture of old and new decorations, some handmade and some that Mum had bought over the years at the different craft fairs she and Dad used to go to. Amidst these smells was the distinct aroma of baking. Mum had clearly been very busy. All the familiar seasonal smells were a welcome distraction from the grey drizzle that had met us as we had driven across the border into Norfolk. But as Mum bustled round us the usual warm glow of being properly home wrapped its delicate arms around me and enveloped me with a feeling of pure joy. The anticipation of spending precious family time with Nathan, the children and Mum helped push away the niggling worrying thoughts that I had recently had about my health. I unconsciously shook my head to rid the thoughts and to get into the Christmas spirit.

As we drove home I asked the children their favourite part of Christmas with Granny and their best presents. This was a post-Christmas tradition that had become part of our family's DNA. First to be asked was always Titch.

She was the youngest of our brood and although christened Kitty we rarely called her by her proper name. She became Titch at quite a young age and was known as that with fondness. The name suited her small stature. She was the petite one of the family who was blessed with long blonde curly hair and the deepest of blue eyes. Titch thought for a moment and then declared that 'everything' was her best bit and that her favourite present was her new pink bike. On Boxing Day morning we had been for a walk along the promenade at the seaside town which is only five minutes from Mum's house. Titch had been desperate to try out her bike and the flat, large expanse away from traffic was the ideal place for her test ride. Her first few attempts were a bit wobbly but she soon gained confidence and was off. Occasionally she had to stop to avoid other walkers, and a few more competent cyclists, but on the whole she did really well.

Next it was Daniel's turn to share his highlights of the holiday. I wondered how he would react to the game this year. He was growing so fast and I wondered whether it would still be cool for a fourteen year old boy to share something like this with his family. But after being invited to share his thoughts, Daniel said that the very best bit of the holiday was when he and Nathan had gone for a long walk through the woods near to Mum's cottage. I recalled the walk they had had late in the afternoon. Daniel had been so excited when they had come home because he had seen the barn owl that lived close to Mum's cottage. He and Nathan had seen it flying silently across the ploughed field and then to their delight it landed on a perch and stayed there for a few minutes. Daniel also remembered that when he had been walking with his Dad they had talked about dreams, hopes and aspirations. Later, Nathan had told me that Daniel's current ambition was to go to university like his older sister Rebecca. He said that he wanted to become a sports coach. We'd always known that he had an aptitude for sport but never that he held hopes of turning his hobby into a career. When pushed about his best present, Daniel had confirmed that it was his new mobile telephone.

Finally it was Rebecca's turn to share her best memory. Rebecca had started university in September and this had been her first holiday home apart from a weekend in November when she had come home for a few days. She said that the best bit was spending time with her family and realising how normal we were. This observation reflected the fact that some of the people she was acquainted with at university appeared to come from avant-garde families whose lives could best be described as colourful. She had shared some stories with me during our Friday night telephone calls and some of them made me blush. I think for Rebecca it was quite an eye-opener. She said that her best presents were a thick woolly jumper that Mum had knitted for her and a matching hot-water bottle cover. Rebecca's room in the accommodation she rented was quite draughty and so the addition of a functional, cosy hot-water bottle was most welcomed.

When the children had finished sharing their best bits of Christmas, Rebecca asked Nathan and me what had been our best presents. Nathan said that spending time with us all was good as was Mum's baking. But he also said that the new Bon Jovi CD we had bought him was very special. He had it playing on the car stereo as we drove home. The lyrics extoling the fact this house was not for sale. As I heard the words for the umpteenth time that week I wondered what meaning they held for us as a family.

I was brought back from my thoughts as I heard Rebecca telling me that it was my time to share my highlights. I desperately wanted to say that for me the most important bit was being with my family and watching the children's excitement. But I thought they would all groan at my sentiments and so, reserving those precious memories for myself, I said that being by the sea and having fun were my best bits.

The chatter in the back of the car continued until Titch fell asleep. I glanced at Nathan and could tell he was concentrating with extra vigilance on his driving. The dark night had taken hold now and with no street lights to help guide us he was reliant on the headlights from our old VW Passat. It had started to drizzle which added to the difficulties of driving along one of the notorious A roads in the district. Motorists were reminded every few miles of the number of fatalities in the past year. The red advisory sign comparing the statistics for the previous year, offering a stark reminder to slow down and drive with more care.

I leaned back in my seat and drifted off into a gentle slumber. I didn't normally like to sleep when Nathan was driving, especially when the conditions were not ideal but the rhythmic swish of the windscreen wipers helped smooth my anxieties and I drifted off to sleep. I dreamt I was a child again back at our family home. In my dream Dad was still the imposing figure I remembered with his flash of auburn hair and his handlebar moustache. I was six again, it was Christmas day and we had just opened our presents following a walk with Chalkie our poodle through the woods that surrounded the village. I recalled, in my dream, how cold it was and how the wind had whipped up the remaining dried and crisp leaves and how they had menacingly danced around my legs, my white ankle socks giving no protection against their flight. Now as I dreamt of that Christmas I could again feel the warmth of the cottage as we walked back into the safe sanctuary of Mum's kitchen. Maybe those ingrained memories were the reason I so liked going home to Mum's at Christmas. In my dream I was ripping the paper away from a large present that had been standing by the Christmas tree when I had woken on Christmas morning. In the dream I could hear the paper ripping as I unceremoniously pulled it away from the box that it was covering. I squealed with delight when I opened the box to reveal its hidden contents – a brand new, shiny doll's house which Dad had made for me in his workshop. The house was perfect, a mini replica of our cottage. Mum had made the soft furnishing for it and had bought me a family of small dolls who fitted in perfectly. I ran over to Mum and Dad and gave them both a big hug. I was the happiest little girl in Norfolk.

Through the kitchen door I could smell the turkey in the range and the roast potatoes cooking in the goose fat that Mum had bought from old Mr Duke our local butcher. Mum and Dad then opened their presents, Dad had bought Mum a silk scarf from one of his trips into Norwich and Mum had knitted Dad a yellow v neck jumper. In addition to Dad's jumper Mum had also knitted me a blue cardigan that had yellow cuffs on the arms and a yellow button band. She had clearly either run out of blue wool or had decided to utilise what she had to save money. Either way I loved my cardigan and remember wearing it until I had out-grown it when I was eight and had a growth spurt.

I winced as I woke from my short but happy sleep. The pain had come back; maybe it was because I had been sitting in the same position for too long. I hoped it was as simple as that. Nathan's peripheral vision must have noticed my sudden wince; he briefly turned to me 'are you okay?'

'Fine thanks just need a stretch.' I said with an over confident smile. Who was I trying to reassure I thought as I moved in the seat to get some comfort.

Thankfully we were near our usual half-way stop and so I was able to have the much needed stretch for five minutes before we carried on north. The drizzle had been replaced with heavier rain. The sky looked dark and oppressive. As we carried on with our homeward bound journey the car's headlights caught the rain as it relentlessly bounced onto the black tarmac. The combination of road noise and rain began to thud in my head to the point where I wanted to scream. I didn't, instead I sat looking out into the dark, wet night and tried to shut out all noise, all thoughts, all everything.

I always felt unsettled on this stretch of the journey; the sea was now far behind us, Mum's village was getting further and further away and the holiday was over. That night the feeling was even more intense than usual. I was conscious that I was going home to a busy few days. The following day I would need to prepare for the end of the school holidays. Titch and Daniel would be returning to school so I would need to make sure that school clothes were ironed, bags packed and lunches prepared. Nathan was also back at work, weather permitting, and so I would need to make sure everything was ready for him too. I was lucky that I had an extra day to prepare for my return but I knew that I would be going back to a busy term. There were new staff due to start in school and that always meant additional work for my administration team. To add to my potential stress, I had seen a post on Facebook from Lizzie my colleague saying how she was hiding under the duvet because she thought she was starting with a chest infection. I had tried to have caring, compassionate thoughts but in reality I felt cross that she was once again indicating sickness just before a new term. Was it only me who had noticed this pattern of sickness, surely the Head had also spotted it?

As we got nearer home the children began to get restless in the back of the car. I smiled to myself as a chorus of 'are we nearly there yet' rang out from Titch and Daniel. They knew this journey very well and knew exactly where we were which therefore did not necessitate their usual question. Nathan and I looked at each other and grinned, maybe their questioning was just another part of our family traditions that I held on to so dearly.

I knew that all three of the children were growing up rapidly and soon they would all be young adults and not my little children. I recalled when Rebecca was born and how I had been, for a few months paralysed with Post Natal Depression. The Health Visitor had been so supportive but I had really struggled to leave the dark place where my hormones had taken me. The time then went so slowly and I recalled desperately wanting Rebecca to grow and develop so that, in my mind, she became a person not a helpless baby. Maybe I had not been ready for motherhood; I felt I had given up so much to become a mum and to enter into the stereotypical expectations of becoming a family. Becoming a mother was a serious role to take on which meant my child-free identity was being taken over by a new and scary one.

Everyone had told me how wonderful it was when we announced that we were going to be parents. It was long before the days of Baby Showers but nevertheless friends and family came bearing gifts and exuding excitement at the prospect of a baby Williamson coming into our lives. *'Oh you will make a lovely mother'* and *'how perfect for the perfect couple'* were typical responses Nathan and I heard over and over again. I smiled and as I gently rubbed my ever growing stomach tried hard to fit into their genuine desires and excitement. And then Rebecca did grow and, in my eyes, became a real person and before I knew it she was off to infant school and then a second wave of depression hit me. The memory of standing outside the school gates once I had dropped her off, in her shiny new shoes and bright yellow mac, and me sobbing had stayed with me all those years. Other mothers were also quietly bemoaning the fact that their offspring were now on the educational treadmill that they would not get off from again until they were practically adults. But it seemed to me that none of them were quite as noisy or dramatic as me in our respective grief. I finally managed to drag myself from the gate and sat for half an hour in my old Mini sobbing great sobs of regret.

I found solace that Rebecca quickly settled into the new routine and took to schooling like the proverbial duck. When she came home from school and regaled Nathan and me with stories of what she had done and what Miss Duncan her teacher had said to her I found peace with the passing of her early years and in those early autumnal days found a new contentment. Thankfully when Daniel and Titch were born I was not troubled with the same maternal indifference and managed to enjoy being a mum.

But now, as I glanced at my brood in the back of the car I felt a tinge of apprehension. They were growing up so fast, we'd already semi-lost Rebecca to university. She would be returning in a couple of weeks for her second term and I somehow doubted I would have her living back at home permanently. I was so proud of her achievements, the first Williamson to go to university and making a big impression already with her studies. Daniel was close behind then there was Titch. I wasn't sure where she would end up; she was highly intelligent but never seemed to apply any academic practice to her school work. She was the arty one of the family with a great panache for creating all manner of craftwork. She reminded me of me when I was her age. I too was always making things and being creative with Mum's cast-off wool and material.

The niggling feeling of worry and doubt came back in a wave as we turned the corner into our cul-de-sac.

'Home sweet home' said Nathan as we pulled on to the drive 'glad to see the milkman hasn't been!'

The children laughed at Nathan's usual joke about the milkman. This family story dated back to when he was a boy and went away with his parents for their annual week by the sea. His mother thought that his father had cancelled the milk; however, his father thought that his mother had so when they arrived home there were seven bottles of silver top on the doorstep. I weakly smiled at the joke, the recurring feelings of worry weighing too heavily on my mind for me to join in as usual. The pain had returned and I was also feeling nauseas. *'Shake it off Angela'* my voice of reason said, *'you're just tired after a lovely time away, pull yourself together woman.'* But another part of me shouted back *'and what was the excuse before we went away?'*

THREE

Angela

I felt anxious as I sat in the waiting room at the GP's surgery. I checked the contents of my handbag to make sure my mobile was inside. *'Calm down'* I kept repeating to myself as I waited alone. The pain had been increasing since we had returned from Mum's. I had decided on Friday that I had to face head on whatever it was and make an appointment to see Dr Woods. My logical half had told me that it was really nothing to worry about and that a few tablets would get me sorted. However, my over-imaginative half was telling me that I needed to be worried and that in days I would be dead if I didn't go to the doctors.

I really didn't like doctor's waiting rooms, there was a clinical presence that was very business-like, everyone spoke in whispers, nobody gave anyone eye contact and there was a sense of helplessness hanging in the room. I remembered all the times I had sat there previously, when I first thought I was pregnant with Rebecca, when I had severe depression after having Rebecca, when Daniel had a chest infection that we couldn't shift, when Nathan was signed off work because of a work-related hernia, the list went on but somehow this time it felt very different and I felt very alone.

The TV monitor was showing a series of short information films which after the first loop became monotonous and lost their credibility. A man in a fireman's uniform told us of the dangers of not checking our smoke alarms regularly or even worse not having any fitted. I wondered whether he was a real fireman or whether he was an actor. I decided the latter and briefly inwardly smiled about his capabilities of throwing me over his shoulder and carrying me to safety. The next film was extolling the virtue of winter health checks for older people. The film showed a gaggle of over 60s on a hike in the countryside. They all looked happy and content with their lot as they set out over the moors. The final film in the trilogy was about baby immunisation and appealed to all new parents to talk to their health visitor for advice.

I looked round at the posters that seemed to fill every spare bit of wall. They all looked cluttered and gave the waiting area an untidy appearance. One typed notice asked patients to turn off their mobile telephones while its neighbour gave the code for free Internet access. I wondered to myself which poster was the accurate one of the two. In the corner there was a bottled water machine half full with water, alongside it was an empty cup dispenser.

I checked my handbag again; yes my mobile was exactly where I had left it. I bottom shuffled on the uncomfortable seat. A young boy behind me found great joy in kicking his feet into the back of my chair. Each thud from his small feet knocked into my back and jolted me. I became increasingly annoyed with his mother who was clearly taking no responsibility for his behaviour. I heard her on her phone talking to a friend about a night out. From her conversation it sounded like she had missed her alcohol intake at Christmas because of being unwell and so had made up for it last night. Her parting line to her friend was that she felt rougher than her son but hoped the doctor wouldn't notice. My cruel side suspected that the doctor would know all about it as she had been so loud on the phone. The rest of the waiting room had heard her colourful description of the night and I guessed her voice would have penetrated the wooden doors that were the barrier between the public area and the private consulting rooms. When she finally dragged herself away from reminiscing about the night she managed to turn her attention to her son and told him off about his kicking. She told him it was annoying her and to give up before she smacked him. Briefly he gave up but soon found the temptation too great and started again. I was relieved when his name flashed across the notice board and he was summoned to see one of the junior partners. I noticed his mother walk unsteadily into the GP's room.

I realised that the persistent kicking and the mother's colourful phone conversation had both been good distractions. Briefly I had been so busy bracing myself for the next kick that I had stopped thinking about why I was sitting alone in a doctor's waiting room. With the removal of the next England mid-fielder I was again back to thinking about my pain and what Dr Woods was going to say to me. I felt frightened and alone and not ready to hear what he was going to say.

FOUR

Nathan

We sat in the waiting room holding hands. I glanced at Angela and a wave of love swept over me. She was dressed smartly in her dark flecked wool jacket, smart brown trousers and brown brogues. I noticed that she was clutching onto her handbag for dear life. She looked smaller than usual and tired. She had kept telling me that she was sleeping but the dark rims under her eyes gave her away. Her beautiful long, blonde hair was tied up in a knot on her head. Usually I liked that style but then it was only emphasising how tired and drawn she looked. She fiddled with her handbag, checking the contents regularly then again gripping the handle tightly with her free hand.

The lyrics from Pink Floyd's song *Time* were invading my head. I could not stop hearing them no matter how hard I tried *'and you run and you run to catch up with the sun but it's sinking...Shorter of breath and one day closer to death'*. *'Go away'* I silently urged but my cruel unconscious mind was not listening.

I hadn't realised until that awful day that one could feel numb and hypervigilant at the same time. Since Angela had told me about her appointment with Dr Woods I had been in an emotional spin. *'Why was this happening to my family? How the hell was I going to manage this? Why, why, why?'*

I'd come home from work that day looking forward to a hot shower, food and a night watching the football. It had been a busy few days since I had returned to work after the Christmas break. I was trying to complete an extension that we had started before Christmas but the bitterly cold weather had been getting in the way. The customers were becoming frustrated with the slow progress and it felt as though I was constantly fire-fighting with them trying to explain that I was not prepared to start laying bricks in the freezing temperatures. Prior to beginning the project we had had that discussion. I had outlined the timeframe for the work and had carefully explained about the implications if the weather turned and explained that they would be living in a building site over the Christmas period. They were insistent that we should begin the project the second week of December and said that they totally understood that there were factors way beyond my control that might impact on the work. So there I was the first week in January, the temperature not getting above freezing, trying to placate two very angry customers and worrying about how I was going to pay my team of bricklayers when it was obvious that we would not be getting the next instalment of money due from the customers until *'we had laid some bloody bricks'*.

'Hello Angela, only me' I shouted as I walked into the house. I was expecting to be greeted by the smell of cooking and the hustle and bustle that was the norm for our house. Instead all was quiet, it was evident that the children were out and I instinctively knew something was wrong. I found Angela in the sitting room curled up on the settee. She had been crying. I went to her and put my arms around her.

'Angela what is it my love?'

Through her sobs she told me about her appointment with Dr Woods and that he had referred her to the local hospital 'as a matter of urgency.' We held each other and I gently kissed her head 'it will be okay' I said with no conviction. My mind was racing as I tried to process the information she had told me in between her uncontrolled crying. I looked across the room towards the now redundant Christmas tree, *'Happy New Year'* I said under my breath.

I was shocked at the speed the hospital appointment had come through. Angela was sent for tests and a scan which had been completed and now we were waiting to hear the news. I began to imagine how people felt when waiting for the judge to pass judgment on them. Now I was in the dock waiting to hear the fate of my wife, our family and me.

The large clock on the wall had a hypnotic tick. The slow measured passing of time being articulated with each passing tick. Pink Floyd's music still invading my every thought. The seconds of my life passing in front of me while I sat in a state of confusion, fear and suspended reality. My old man had instilled into me from an early age that as a male I had responsibilities to be the provider and protector of my family. When I was eight he died following an accident at work. Two days before he died, when the doctors knew they could do no more for him, he held my hand, looked me in the eye and told me that I was the man of the house now and that I needed to look after my Mum and kid brother. That was one hell of a responsibility for an eight year old but because I loved my Dad and respected him so much I was prepared, in my childlike state, to take on the mantel and become the man of the house. The belief was hardwired into my brain, my primary responsibility and duty in life was to care for and be the provider for my family.

For the first time in my life I felt that that role was too great, I couldn't step up to the mark this time. I felt utterly impotent. I loved Angela more than anything and I was scared I was not going to live up to my expectations. My role had been taken away from me in one big, cruel act.

We were ushered into the consultant's small room by a nurse. She smiled and apologised for the delay, explaining that Mr Gough had been called to an emergency on the wards. She looked business like; to her this was just one of many consultations each day and we were just a name on a piece of paper. She did not know our history, our family story, our hopes and fears. She was a small-bit actor in this play that was unfolding, hers was a small part, quite insignificant really in the grand scheme of things but nevertheless right now she was part of our story. She sat slightly behind Angela and me. I noticed her casually cross her legs at her ankles. I wondered how many times she had sat there and how many different scenarios she had witnessed.

Mr Gough looked up as we walked into the room, he offered us both his hand which we duly shook. I think he passed some observation about the weather being particularly cold but all I heard was noise. '*Get on with it man*' I thought, '*tell us what we want to hear, give Angela a prescription and let us get back on with our life after this minor hiccup*'. I was aware of the clock in his room ticking to the same rhythm as the one in the waiting room. Time again ticking away to make up a dull day.

Mr Gough moved uncomfortably in his seat 'I've looked at all the results, there is no easy way to say this, I'm really sorry but...'

Angela let out a brief sob then went quiet as the news began penetrating her being 'what about my babies' she whispered, 'what do I tell my babies?'

FIVE

Rebecca

Dad knocked on the bedroom door 'can I come in Sweetheart?'

He came in and looked at the bags on my bed and the pile of clothes waiting to be packed.

'All set then for going back eh?' he asked in a nonchalant manner that I knew was masking his sadness. He'd been really upset last term when I left home for the start of my university course. I think in some respects it was a bigger wrench for Dad than it was for Mum. We'd driven all the way in near silence with just the occasional Williamson banter that was typical of our family. When we had got to university I remember experiencing similar feelings to those I had had when I started at infant school all those years ago. I had never told Mum but I watched her walk down the school drive and past the big iron gates. I knew she was crying and I so wanted to run after her and cry with her. I stood by the window crying and feeling very alone. Miss Duncan, my teacher, had been kind and had held my hand and taken me to the table where there had been an assortment of coloured crayons and paper. The distraction of doing a drawing 'for Mummy' worked for a while as I became engrossed in the picture of my family.

When Mum came to collect me at 3.00pm I was excited to tell her all about my day, the new friends I had made and the big boy who was unkind and had pulled my pigtails.

Mum said she was pleased that I had had a lovely day and that maybe tomorrow the big boy wouldn't be so unkind. Tomorrow? That was a shock to my five year old illogical capacity, but I'd been, did I really have to go back?

Now Mum and Dad were about to leave me again but this time in a small room at the end of a very long corridor. The room was functional; I had a small desk, a bed, wardrobe and comfy, red leather effect, chair. The window looked over a car park. In the far distance I could see a hill with trees on it and if I really peered out could see solitary birds soaring above the green roof of trees. Sometimes during the first few weeks of the semester I would look at the birds and envy their freedom. They looked so peaceful as they caught the thermals and climbed ever upwards into the autumnal sky.

After a few weeks of being really homesick I managed to turn my loneliness around. I joined some of the activity clubs and began to make friends. One girl, Cassie, who lived on the same landing as me became a source of support. She too was feeling anxious at the prospect of being away from her family. We found we shared a love of hot chocolate and so whenever possible went to a small independent café which served the most delicious drinks. It was on the outskirts of the city and was a welcome distraction. We soon became known there and if we went when a certain young man was working we were guaranteed extra marshmallows on top of our drinks. I teased Cassie that he had a crush on her which she protested at loudly. However, she was happy to maintain his dreams for the sake of our free marshmallows. Our trips there in the first term were something to look forward to and I was looking forward to seeing Cassie again following the Christmas break. We had kept in contact during the holidays via Facebook. So I knew about her Christmas, the big fall out with her on off boyfriend and her Mum's drunken New Year's Eve party which sounded like utter mayhem.

'Are you going to take good care of yourself?'

'Dad' I said hesitantly, 'I don't want to go back.'

There I'd said it. Even the prospect of hot chocolate, seeing Cassie and getting back into my studies did not help stop me worrying about returning. Since we had been back from Gran's I had started to feel less and less inclined to go back and to leave home. Initially it had just been the feeling of not wanting to go back after a lovely time at home with my crazy, noisy family but then I started to worry that there was something wrong with Mum. I'd not shared these worries with anyone it was just a feeling. I had noticed when we were away that she looked more tired than usual and that she didn't seem herself.

Also Dad seemed a bit different too and I knew he and Mum had been somewhere the previous day. When they had eventually got home I thought Mum had been crying and Dad was upset too. What if they'd reached a bad patch in their marriage and were thinking about separating? How would we cope, I'd be okay because of being older but what about Daniel and Titch? Or maybe Dad's work had dried up and they were worried about paying the mortgage and all the bills.

Dad looked at me, 'I know Sweetheart, I wish we could have another few days too but you'll be okay when you get back. That girl, what is her name? Cassie isn't it, she'll be there and you'll soon be back in a routine with your studies. Are you worried about the exams that are coming up? You'll be fine you know you will, you've had your head in a book most of the holidays.'

I was angry with Dad. He wasn't listening to what I was saying. He was assuming my anxieties were about going back, which in part they were, but they were deeper than that. I instinctively knew something was happening in our family and the two adults were keeping me in the dark. I was annoyed that sometimes they expected me to be an adult and give me adult responsibilities but then when something important was happening they treated me like a child again.

'What's wrong Dad, I know something is so please don't try and hide it, what's going on?'

Dad stared out of the window and aimlessly started to fold my jumpers which were strewn over the bed. 'What do you mean?' he eventually asked.

'Dad, I'm not stupid, I can tell there is something wrong, are you and Mum splitting up?' I tried hard to fight the rising lump in my throat.

Dad now looked me in the eye. 'What? No of course we're not splitting up what on earth made you think that?'

'I know something is happening.'

Dad looked away again. 'What do you think is happening Becks' he asked.

'I don't know but I know something is and I feel I should be at home and not all those miles away stuck in my prison cell away from everyone.'

'Is it so horrible there?'

I desperately wanted to say that it was awful at university with the hope that Dad would tell me it was okay and that I didn't need to go back, but I didn't. That would have been a lie, it wasn't that bad really and I was finding it easier. But right now there was something happening and I didn't know what it was. I shook my head and looked down at my feet. I realised I'd got odd socks on, a bright pink spotty one and a yellow, stripy one. Normally I would have laughed and passed some comment about having an identical pair but I didn't. Right now wasn't the time for joking about something as silly as a pair of socks.

Dad coughed to clear his throat and then reached over to hold my hand. My stomach summersaulted as I knew he was going to tell me what was happening. Did I really want to hear this? Was I ready to hear something awful?

'It's absolutely nothing to worry about but you know how Mum has been a bit under the weather recently well she's had some tests and is ill. But it really is nothing to worry about and by the time you're home for Easter everything will be back to normal.'

'What is it Dad, what is wrong?' I asked as tears streamed down my face.

I could taste the salty mixture on my lips and in that moment felt as though my world had been turned upside down. But my upset very quickly turned to anger 'you weren't going to tell me were you?' I shouted at him 'you were just going to let me go back and not bother to tell me, like I'm not that important and it doesn't matter.'

Dad tried to put his arm round my shoulder but I shrugged him away. My mind was racing; I needed information but at the same time didn't want to know anymore. I tried to calm myself and asked again in a more controlled way 'what is it Dad, what is wrong with Mum?'

Dad tried to explain about IT and that it was nothing to worry about and that after some treatment Mum would be okay. He said that he and Mum had been to the hospital the previous day and had had a conversation with the consultant. After that they had been for a long walk back through the park and had talked and talked about the news. He said that they had discussed about what they should say to us, and that their priority was to make sure that the illness didn't impact on us three children. He said they had decided that they would not tell me anything because of me going back to university. They were going to let me settle back and also get my exams out of the way and then would have come to stay for the weekend like they did last term. He said they were going to tell me then. He also said that they had agreed not to say anything to Daniel and Titch because they were too young to understand and didn't therefore need to know.

I tried to understand what Dad had just said. Firstly Mum was poorly and secondly they were not going to tell any of us children. Did they really think we were all so stupid that we wouldn't have guessed something was wrong? I'd already guessed and I suspected that Daniel also knew but was too afraid to ask.

Dad pulled me closer to him and kissed the top of my head. 'It will be alright Becks' he said as he stroked the top of my hair, 'trust me it will all be okay.'

SIX

Nathan

Following the arrival of IT I had been trying to juggle work and being at home to care for Angela. I was increasingly feeling torn between wanting to be at home to look after her and the need to carry on working. Because I had a good team of lads working for me on the whole it wasn't too bad and I managed to keep on top of the work while also being where I wanted to be.

We had finally managed to finish the extension in late January. That was the one that we had started just before Christmas and which had given me a load of ear-ache from the customers. They moaned about every step of the project and were constantly on the phone to me complaining about how the work was developing. When we were unable to work because of the bitterly cold snap they were not happy. When we were working in the rain they were not happy because the lads were *'trampling mud everywhere'* and when we were close to completion they were not happy because we had taken so long. I was beginning to lose patience with them and on a number of occasions felt like telling then where to put their extension. I was quite used to difficult customers having been in the business for so long but because of everything else that was happening I really struggled with their attitude. I was tired and anxious and my mind was always with Angela and not on customer relations. Their attitude was just what I didn't need at that time so it was with a sense of relief when we finally finished the job. As soon as we left the site I took the lads to the pub for a celebratory pint; they deserved it.

We had other jobs waiting to be started but these were all quite small and not too time consuming. That was good as it gave me some leeway to be at home, however the downside was less work meant less money. I began to dread looking at the bank statement because, for the first time in my working life there was more money going out than coming in. Initially when Angela was signed off from work she still got her full pay but I was conscious that that would not be the case for long. I tried not to share my concerns with her but I think she knew that our financial situation was not as good as we would have liked it to be.

As the work was beginning to slow down I had a telephone call from a potential customer who had been recommended by Mr and Mrs Maune. They were customers that we had done a lot of work for previously. Last year we had done an extension for them and it had been a very lucrative contract. I'd worked hard to win the tender but I think through a combination of having a good reputation and being competitive with pricing we had secured the work. It had been a joy to work with them. They were clear what they wanted and had been happy to let us get on with what we were doing. Every morning when we arrived on site there were mugs of tea waiting for us and quite often homemade cakes for our mid-morning break. We had joked with them that we didn't want that job to end as they looked after us so well. Apparently Mr Maune had been talking to his friend about our work and how pleased he had been with the extension. He had given this new customer my phone number and had suggested that it would be worth him seeing if I would take the work on.

The new customer wanted a two storey extension to the side of his house and a single storey wrap-round at the rear of the house. It looked on paper as though it would be quite straightforward. There was sufficient access and no worries about existing drains or tree roots which was always something I had to consider. From the initial telephone conversation I estimated that if we took on the job it would provide a good five or six months of work. That was good as it would offer the team some security and also be a regular income. But I had concerns about even giving the customer a quote. He lived about an hour's drive away from our house and not only would we have to contend with rush-hour traffic through the city every day we would also have to add in additional time for the rural part of the journey too. Normally that would not be a consideration; we had worked away from home before and managed the travelling without any problems. But this time I had big reservations. It would add an extra two hours to the day and what if I needed to get home quickly to Angela? Sometimes with smaller jobs, or when the lads were well on with the work I felt confident that I didn't need to be on site all the time but with such a big job I knew I would have to be there more often than not. And because of the distance it wasn't as though I could even pop home at lunch time to check on Angela.

I was in a real dilemma, what on earth should I do? I knew that it would be really bad to turn down work, especially when it was a piece of work based on a recommendation. Uncle Bob, who had taken me on as a young lad, used to instil in me the need to nurture good customers as they were the ones that you could rely on again and again. So if I turned down this opportunity Mr Maune might not recommend me again. Also if I turned it down I would be letting the team down, after all they all relied on me to pay their wages. They all had mortgages or rent to pay and young families to support so a guaranteed income for a few months was not to be dismissed lightly. And if I did turn it down I would be letting my family down too. We too needed to pay the mortgage and all the bills and it was down to me to be the provider, I was the man of the house after all.

But I didn't want to be so far away from home. What if Angela needed me, what if she was feeling really ill and I was needed at home to care for her. What if she was ill and couldn't pick Titch up from school? If I was on a job close to home I could leave it and get home quickly but with this one it would not be so easy.

I postponed telephoning the customer back; I needed time to think about what I was going to do but I really didn't know. I kept trying to weigh up the pros and cons but just could not find the answer. Normally when I had a problem I would talk it through with Angela and we would find a solution together. That was how we worked and was one of the reasons why our relationship was so strong. But I was scared to talk about this one with her. I knew she would say that I needed to take the job and carry on as normal. She was trying hard to maintain the life we had known before IT and this included pretending that everything was okay. I knew that if I even mentioned not taking the work she would be really angry with me. It would be a sign that things were not normal. It would be a clear indication that our family life had changed to such an extent that even work was being adversely affected by IT.

Should I risk taking it on and hope that I didn't have to let the customer down, and with it my reputation. Or should I risk not taking it and jeopardise my reputation.

We needed the money, but I needed to be with Angela. What on earth should I do?

SEVEN

Rebecca

The train was slightly delayed as I headed home for the weekend. It was busy, full of Friday night commuters all jostling for their space in the packed carriages. Thankfully I had managed to get a seat by the window. I was quickly joined by a woman 'is this seat taken love?' she asked. I confirmed that it was free and she sat next to me, squeezing into the seat along with her bulging bags of shopping. 'That's better' she said as she wriggled in her seat to get comfortable. 'Been on my feet all day, but it was a good shop' she commented as she patted her bags with gleeful satisfaction. She proceeded to open her capacious handbag and after a few minutes of rifling through the contents found a battered looking sandwich. I could sense a feeling of satisfaction when she had retrieved the sad looking contents of the sandwich bag and started to devour the limp white bread. I wasn't sure what the filling was, it was difficult to discern from the limited information I had. I couldn't actually see the contents nor was there any smell to give me a hint. What I could ascertain was that my travelling companion found it very tasty as she greedily ate it.

'Oh that's better' she said as she finished the last mouthful of her sandwich. I wondered unkindly whether my journey home was going to be peppered with the observation *'oh that's better'*. I smiled at her but quickly looked away, not really wanting to get into a conversation. I looked at the couple sitting opposite me. They too had got on after me and had both quickly got their tablets out and were now checking emails. The woman was tall and thin, I decided that she must work in an office, possibly as a manager. The man with her, I presumed also worked alongside her. They clearly knew each other and their work-related conversations suggested that they worked together. They didn't see me looking at them and didn't, thankfully, engage in any conversations with me. All the way home they were engrossed in their emails.

The Guard's voice came over the tannoy as he apologised for the delay. He went on to explain that it was due to an earlier breakdown further up the line. The shopping lady groaned 'that's all we need, I'm going to miss my connection now. Where are you off to love?'

I told her that I was going home for the weekend to see my parents. 'That's nice' she observed, 'are you at university down here?' she asked.

I confirmed that I was. I hoped that she would not get into a conversation about my course or about home life. I didn't really feel like getting into a conversation with a stranger, I wanted to look out of the window, watch the world go by and count the minutes to getting home. Thankfully before she could ask any more questions the train slowly started to pull out of the station. I turned my head to look out of the window and hoped that my actions would give her a clear message that I didn't want to talk. I smiled to myself thinking that maybe the psychology lecture that Cassie had dragged me to had been useful after all. She had only wanted to go to the evening event because she had heard that the lecturer had a good reputation for public speaking and was also rather good looking. I had teased Cassie about this but as I had nothing else on that night I was reluctantly dragged along. To my surprise I actually really enjoyed it, and yes he was a very enigmatic speaker. He was talking about body-language and non-verbal communication and it all made sense what he was saying. Now as I carefully moved my body slightly to the right I hoped I was putting into practice what he had been lecturing about.

As the train gathered speed there was the usual announcement, welcoming us on board and informing us which service it was and where the next station stop would be. That announcement was quickly followed by the On Board Catering Team announcing that the buffet car was open serving a selection of hot and cold drinks, alcohol, sandwiches, cakes and snacks. There was an apology, but due to the number of passengers the refreshments trolley would not be able to make its way through the carriages. My temporary neighbour groaned 'I was dying for a cuppa as well' she commented. I just smiled mildly and, practising more of my non-verbal body language shrugged my shoulders as if to sympathise with her.

I decided that looking out of the window might not work as a ploy to avoid conversations so I reached for my rucksack that was on the floor between my legs and pulled out a text book. I did have all good intentions to read it but the train's rhythmic movement had a hypnotic effect and I could feel my eyes getting heavier. I didn't want to fall asleep so I put my book away and reached for a magazine that I had bought on impulse at the station. I thought Mum would enjoy looking at it too and so justified the £4.99 price tag.

Thankfully at the next station the shopping lady got off for her connection 'bye love, have a lovely weekend' she said as she hauled herself out from her seat, manoeuvring past the table and gathering all her bags.

'Bye' I said 'hope you manage to get your connection'.

Her seat was quickly re-occupied by a young man with headphones stuck in his ears. He didn't give me eye contact and, for the rest of the journey home I didn't need to employ my newly found psychological skills. I did send Cassie a text though saying how the time with the sexy lecturer had paid off. Her reply was simply three question marks and a smiley face.

When the train was twenty minutes from home, I sent Dad a text, as arranged, to let him know I was nearly back. I felt a growing excitement rising as we were getting closer. I wondered who would be at the station to meet me. I knew Dad would be, he had to be with the car, but I wondered whether Titch or Daniel would be there too. I suspected Titch would be. I had heard her excitement when I had phoned home on Wednesday to see whether it would be okay to go home. I knew that Titch was missing me nearly as much as I was missing her. As we pulled into the station I strained my eyes, scanning the platform to see if I could see my family. Sure enough just by the steps were Dad and Titch, standing on the platform holding hands. I could hardly wait for the train doors to be released so that I could open them and have the hugs that I had been so waiting for.

'Titch' I shouted as I nearly fell out of the door in my excitement. She let go of Dad's hand and came running across the platform to me, dodging the other passengers as she came. She flung her arms round me and gave me a massive squeeze. Dad quickly joined us and also gave me a big squeeze and a kiss.

'Hello Princess' he said, 'by you're looking well, come on let's get you home for dinner.'

Titch insisted that I sat in the back of the car with her; she held my hand tightly and didn't stop talking all the way home. Dad looked at me through his rear-view mirror. He smiled 'somebody has missed you!' he said with a wink.

It was so lovely to be home. Mum looked less tired than the last time I had seen her and she looked better that I had dared to hope. My excitement at coming home for the weekend had been tempered by concerns about what I would find. When I had spoken to Mum last week she had said that she was feeling much better and that was in part what had prompted me to decide to have a weekend back with my family. I wanted and needed to see for myself how she was. But still the constant worry of how she was responding to the treatment was always at the back of my mind.

After a quick hug from everyone, except Daniel of course, Mum announced, with a hint of mischievousness in her voice, that she didn't feel like cooking and so we would have to make do with a take-away. Titch screamed with delight at the prospect. One of my special memories of my teenage years was the Friday night treat of a Chinese take-away. We didn't have it every week but it was a regular feature. With Mum and Dad both working it was convenient for us to order a take-away as a celebration to start the weekend. We all tended to order the same dishes, then Mum would telephone the local Chinese restaurant and order the meal and Dad and I would go to collect it.

Sometimes, when we were having an extra special treat we would be allowed to eat it in the living room while watching TV. This was always a marker of a very special occasion as there was an unwritten rule that we always sat down for meals, as a family, and at the dining table. As a teenager, I used to envy my friends who talked about eating meals ad hoc and with no routines or convention. It seemed to me, as I was growing up, that that was something to aspire to, but now that I was away from home and more often than not ate alone in my room I valued so much the importance that Mum and Dad placed on eating together. Our Friday treat was one of the many things that I missed about not being at home, but I also knew from conversations that since Mum had been ill it had become less and less.

While Dad went out to pick up the take-away I dumped my washing into the machine and sorted out my rucksack. I gave Mum the magazine I had bought for her and we sat together at the kitchen table flicking through it. We didn't have long to read it as Dad was back quickly with the familiar brown paper bags holding the delicious smells of our food. Mum, as always served it on to our plates and then, looking at Dad suggested that we ate it in the room while watching a film. I thought Titch was going to burst with excitement at the prospect, but she managed to contain herself.

So my impromptu weekend home couldn't have had a better start. We all sat in silence as we ate our meals. I'm not sure how much of the beginning of the film we saw; we were all too busy savouring our treat. I know the food was important but I also think there was something symbolic about the normality of the occasion. Cassie's sexy lecturer had talked in his lecture about symbolism and again for the second time that evening I could relate to what he had said. For a brief period we were doing really normal, mundane stuff that meant so much to each of us and which acted as a reminder of small chunks of life that represented our family and who we were.

* * *

The following morning I woke early; I could hear someone in the kitchen and was aware of the smell of a cooked breakfast drifting up the stairs. In the kitchen I found Mum preparing breakfast.

'Morning Becks, thought we might have the works this morning.'

I was happily shocked to see how well she looked and how normal this all seemed.

'Mum' I said hesitantly, 'I don't suppose you fancy going into town with me this morning do you? I'd like to buy a dress for my interview next week and would appreciate your opinion.'

And so after breakfast Dad dropped Mum and me off in town to go shopping. Titch made brief protestations that she hadn't been invited to join us but these quickly disappeared when Dad promised her and Daniel a trip to the local swimming pool.

Mum and I headed to the department store that had been in town for as long as I could remember. We browsed round the different stores within the store and I found a few dresses that I thought might be appropriate for my forthcoming interview and that would be good to wear afterwards as well. I tried two on that I particularly liked. They were both in the sale which made them even more appealing. Mum gave me her opinion about them and we opted for the second one. It was a navy blue spotted dress with three quarter sleeves. Mum liked that one because she thought it would go well with my navy jacket. She also observed that I could 'dress it up or down.' It was really good to get Mum's opinion. Before IT came along she always took a real pride in her appearance and had a good sense of fashion. Probably for the first time I was aware that this shopping trip was less like a mother and daughter outing and more like two equals sharing some time together.

Once the dress had been purchased I suggested that we went to our favourite café in town for a drink. I was conscious that although Mum looked well I didn't want to tire her out and thought that a sit down and a drink might help. It was busy in 'our' café but we managed to get a table for two near the back. I insisted that I bought the coffees so Mum sat and saved the table for us while I queued for the drinks.

'So my love, are you all ready for this interview?' Mum asked.

I told her that I was as ready as I would ever be and that I felt happier now that I had an outfit for it. Since going to university it had been my intention to get a part time job to help pay for my fees and everything. In the first term I had tentatively looked but had not felt confident enough to actually apply for anything, and nothing had really appealed. But the other week I spotted an advertisement for a part-time assistant at the local museum and art gallery which was quite close to the university campus. I had made enquiries and found that the hours would fit well with my studies. The person I spoke to told me that the job would be mainly working in the café but there might also be duties in the gift shop too. To my delight I was invited to attend for an interview. Hence the need for a smart dress.

After our coffee, Mum and I slowly made our way back up the High Street to meet Dad for our lift home. We sauntered up the street looking in the different shops. As we passed the old fashioned sweet shop I was inevitably drawn in by the myriad of glass jars containing every kind of sweet delight you could think of. I bought a quarter of liquorice ones for Dad, a quarter of jelly ones for Titch and a quarter of chocolate ones for Daniel. For Mum I bought a bar of her favourite chocolate. I resisted temptation and didn't buy myself anything. Knowing that I had a lovely new dress to fit into, I left the shop feeling very virtuous.

We hadn't been on the bench at the top of the High Street long when Dad pulled up, 'taxi for the ladies' he shouted as we walked over to him. Titch was buzzing with excitement following her swim; she had managed two lengths of the pool by herself and was very proud of her achievement. She clearly hadn't done such a good job at getting dry or dressed. Her hair was still wet and there was a very strong smell of chlorine in the car.

'Nathan' Mum said disapprovingly, 'you could have made sure she got dried properly, you know how bad her skin is when she doesn't dry herself properly.'

'Sorry love.' was Dad's response.

Thankfully Mum didn't continue with the reprimand, instead she focussed on Titch, telling her that she needed to have a shower as soon as we got home.

After lunch and once Titch was suitably washed and dried I suggested that she and I go for a walk. I invited Daniel too but he was going to meet his friends and so declined the offer. Titch jumped at the chance. We headed for the local park where there were some climbing frames, an assortment of swings and a slide. Titch opted for the swings so I dutifully pushed her to get some momentum going. She swung higher and higher, kicking her legs to help get the swing to move and squealing with pleasure. 'Hold on tight' I shouted to her, my words being carried by the breeze. I stopped myself as I realised how much like Mum I sounded. The thought briefly stopping me in my tracks. For the second time that day I realised that I was no longer a young person, I was a woman and more importantly I was becoming a replica of Mum.

When Titch had had enough on the swings we had a quick go on the slide then went for a walk across the park to see if the horses were in the adjacent field. I thought about how many times we had done this as a family. Our post lunch walk on Sundays was often through the park, over the fields and then back along by the river. For a short period when I was a teenager, I used to try anything I could to get out of the walk. It became a drudge and I couldn't see the point in it. I suspect I made my views very apparent to Mum and Dad, but thankfully that grumpy period didn't last long and as I grew older I began to cherish it more.

I wanted to ask Titch about things at home, I was really keen to know from her child like view what was happening and how she was but I decided not to ask. We'd had a lovely weekend, it had been like old times and right now I didn't want to spoil that, for me or for Titch.

* * *

We all stood on the platform at the railway station waiting for my train. Mum had insisted on packing me up with enough food to last a month. So along with my rucksack containing my freshly laundered washing and my shopping bag with the interview dress safely wrapped inside, I was also heading back to university with a holdall full of food and toilet rolls. The last hour, had as always, been the worst. We had all sat after lunch watching the clock and waiting for it be time for me to leave. We'd had a quiet Sunday morning not doing much really, just pottering. Granny had telephoned and so I had had a long conversation with her. She was filling me in with all the news from her village and I told her all my news from university.

After lunch I helped Dad wash up and tidy the kitchen. We were both unusually quiet and said little. I couldn't decide whether it was because Dad was sad that I was going back or whether it was the uncomfortableness that IT had brought to our family. The elephant was definitely in the kitchen when we were washing up. I commented to Dad about how good Mum was looking and asked whether there was news about the treatment. He didn't say much, other than everybody was happy with how things were going. I didn't push it; I didn't want to ask anymore. For now Mum was looking well and so hopefully that was a positive to hold on to as I headed back to university.

The train arrived on time and I quickly said my last goodbyes to everyone. Titch gave me a squeeze and told me she loved me, Mum and Dad both kissed me and told me to be careful and Daniel sort of said an embarrassed good bye. They all stood waving as the train left the platform and gathered speed; I waved back until the small dots that were my family disappeared in the distance. With a lump in my throat, I managed to find a seat in the first carriage and sat looking out of the window. Why did lovely weekends have to end so soon? What would Cassie's sexy lecturer have had to say about that from his psychological perspective?

EIGHT

Angela

Since the diagnosis I had been trying to maintain a normal a life as possible, not only for the children and Nathan but also for me. Part of that included meeting up whenever possible with my girlfriends. I didn't have a big circle of friends but the three I did have were very special and I treasured their friendships deeply. All three were very different and each had their own traits that I could so easily identify with. There was Elspeth who lived close to us. We met at the local carer and toddler group when I took Rebecca along to help her socialise and for me to meet other new mums. Elspeth and I connected immediately. She too had found it difficult to cope following the birth of her son and our shared experiences meant that we were able to understand each other. In addition she had a similar dry sense of humour and we could both see the funny side of things that perhaps were less clear to other people. Elspeth was the one I turned to most when I needed a cup of tea and a sympathetic ear. Her sage advice had been invaluable over the last few months and I wasn't sure what I would have done without her. Elspeth worked at the local hospital in the records department and generally worked twilight hours so that she could be at home during the day for her two children, not that her eldest really needed her to be there anymore.

Tracey was another one of those friends that would drop everything if she thought I needed some support. She too lived close by and worked from home as a professional blogger writing about knitting and crafting. Whereas Elspeth was a listener, Tracey was a doer and had on many occasions turned up at our house with a homemade shepherd's pie or an apple tart. When I was feeling particularly rough she was the one that came round twice a week to clean the house and do the ironing. No amount of protestations from me stopped her. She took charge of all things domestic and helped maintain some control of the chores. She said it was her way of feeling useful and of doing something.

It was Tracey who suggested being the link person between Titch's school and home. When I was going through the really rough period I was finding it increasingly difficult to always get to school to collect Titch at home-time. I remember one particular day when I had been so ill I could not muster the strength to drive to school. In a frantic phone call I spoke to the head teacher to explain my predicament but she was unable to offer any support. She reassured me that she would look after Titch until I could find someone to collect her. But that didn't really help, in my pain ridden state I couldn't think straight and couldn't work out who there was to collect her. Had I been more coherent I would have tried to contact Nathan, but I knew he was trying to finish a job where there had been problems with the contractors. Mum was back in Norfolk and our neighbours were out at work. In a frantic state I telephoned Tracey to see if she could offer any suggestions. We both laughed later at the stupidity of it, she was the obvious person to ask but my illogical mind had not thought of her. She gladly went to school and safely brought Titch home; telling her that she was doing me a favour while I had a rest.

A few days later when I was feeling a little better Tracey called round with a plan. She said she had been thinking about me and decided that what I needed was to have a support team 'Team Angela' as she called it. She retrieved a piece of paper from her handbag and started exploring with me who I could call on for support in case of an emergency. She then carefully listed their contact details and created a group list on my mobile phone so that I could easily contact them. With her usual efficiency she then contacted them on my behalf and invited them to join the team. She designated herself as chief school collector and with that got me to telephone Titch's school and give the secretary her details ensuring the secretary knew that in an emergency she was the designated person to collect Titch. Tracey then asked for some note paper and deftly wrote a note to Titch about how much she had enjoyed collecting her from school and recalling the fun they had had driving home singing. Tracey ended the note saying that if I was a bit poorly again she would collect Titch from school and they would have another lovely time.

Tracey's pragmatic approach didn't end there. She then helped me to think what Titch and Daniel would need if they had to stay, at short notice, at her house. I think she recognised my unease in contemplating the planning for such a crisis. She leaned across the kitchen table and held my hand 'hopefully Ange we won't ever need to use this but let's do it anyway, just in case.'

I nodded in agreement but it still felt very uncomfortable. While I sat and considered the implications of this, Tracey made another cup of tea and found some digestive biscuits in the cupboard. As she put them on the table she glanced over at me 'thinking power' she said, followed by 'sorry Weight Watchers, guess I won't be your star pupil again this week.'

I marvelled at Tracey's systematic approach to the exercise. She carefully considered the children's needs 'now then' she said 'remind me what Titch and Daniel like for their supper drink?'

When I had given her this information we moved on to bedtime routines for them, even down to whether Titch had a teddy bear that she liked to take to bed with her. Tracey explored all the options so that if she did have to look after the children at short notice she would be able to make their stay as comfortable and as much like home as possible. Although it was a difficult thing to think about it was also really reassuring that in the event of me having a medical crisis things were safely in place for the children.

My third friend, Betty was also my oldest. We'd been friends since primary school and although I didn't see her very often we did keep in contact. Betty lived in London with her businessman husband. Much as Mum loved Nathan I did sometimes wonder whether she still would have preferred me to follow Betty's chosen path. Betty had the life-style that I once, briefly, dreamt about. She lived in a very tidy apartment and had regular meals out. She went on exotic holidays and drove a sports car. Last year I visited Betty and stayed overnight with her and her husband. It was lovely to see her after so many years and we had lots and lots of catching up to do. Inevitably we talked about our school days in Norfolk and the mischief we somehow managed to get up to. We talked about our families and our hopes as we were getting older. As the white wine flowed we laughed, cried and made plans. It was a good evening, but as I caught the train north, the following day, from Kings Cross I felt a wave of relief that I was heading back to my family and my lifestyle.

I didn't tell Betty straight away about IT. I felt that because of her being so many miles away it wasn't necessary to burden her with the worry of what might happen. It was only as I realised that I was not responding to the initial treatment as Mr Gough had hoped that I thought it was only right to tell her. It was a difficult telephone call; how do you angle the conversation round to the fact that you are living with an illness that is potentially going to kill you, especially when your friend is some 200 miles away? I rehearsed what I was going to say and started to dial her number three times before I plucked up the courage to actually go through with the call. We chatted about life, the weather and the awful new waiter that had been employed at her local restaurant. However, Betty being an intuitive type recognised that I hadn't really telephoned for a natter. 'How are you really?' she asked after a few minutes.

'Mmm, not sure how to tell you this one but I'm not doing too good at the moment' was my reply.

The phone went quiet as Betty tried to take in the news. Her first reaction was that she would travel up to Yorkshire the next day. I managed to persuade her that that was not necessary and that actually I would prefer to see her when I was feeling better. I think there was some relief in her voice at that.

The following day Betty rang me to say that she had tracked down a consultant who had an excellent reputation for treating IT. He had a private practice and she could arrange for me to see him by the end of the week. She went on to say that she would worry about his consultation fees 'and everything'. I was hugely touched by her kindness but also angry that she had assumed that I would not be able to afford to go private. Nathan and I had talked about the possibility of finding someone who might just be able to do more than Mr Gough but after much searching of the Internet, we decided that it was a pointless exercise. After the conversation with Betty I mentioned her offer to Nathan. The thought of finding someone who might throw us a proverbial life-line was very tempting, after all this was my life we were talking about and was possibly a glimmer of hope. However, our pride would not allow us to even contemplate having charity from Betty; even though it was the kindest sort of charity meant with true friendship.

Then there were the peripheral friends, the ones on the side-lines who you would pass the time of day with but who would not be included in the more meaningful conversations that proper friends have together. Some of the mums at Titch's school fitted into that category. We would all stand at the school gate every afternoon and engage in meaningless chatter about the state of parking round by the school, the litter that was a regular feature and, for some, the well-toned body of Mike the school caretaker. Some of the mums had seen him at the local gym and took delight in reporting back about his amazing physique and what, in their fantasies, they would like to do with him. I must admit after hearing these conversations I did, very briefly, look at him in a different light but decided that at my age I should know better.

Since IT had come on the scene there had been a mixed response from the other mothers. Initially I didn't say anything to them about being ill; preferring to carry on as normal as Nathan and I had agreed. However, as the treatment took hold and I began having more and more symptoms and side-effects the inevitable conversations started. At first I was not included in these conversations but was aware that some of the huddled groups of mums were speculating about what was happening to me. The clues were there, the glances in my direction and the abrupt silences when I was in earshot. From their behaviour I was able to begin to understand how people with a disability or any minority group might feel. It might have been my increased sensitivity but I started to feel as though their eyes were always watching me, trying to find clues for the changes in my appearance. I began to feel paranoid that everyone was talking about me and making their own assessments about what was wrong.

I did tell a handful of the mums about IT. They had been asking me how I was, knowing full well that I was off work sick. I decided that if I didn't tell them they would make their own conclusions and fuel the rumours that were going round. So I told them. They all said how sorry they were and offered to help in any way, but I sort of knew that their offers of help were perfunctory and didn't hold a great deal of substance. I graciously thanked them and said all the right things about how horrible it was but that we were fine and were managing well.

After coming out they all seemed to give me a slightly wider berth than before. Maybe they were worried about what to say to me, or concerned that I would ask for help or maybe they just wanted to pretend that serious illness was not knocking so close to home. Let's face it, it is not something we want to have to think about.

NINE

Rebecca

'Mum, it's me, I've got the job.'

'Becks, well done you, what did they say to you, when do you start? Nathan, it's Rebecca, she's got the job.'

My excitement at being offered the job at the museum was nearly matched by Mum's. I couldn't wait to telephone her after I had received the call from Dave the manager of the Corporate and Retail Section of the city's museum and art gallery. I thought the interview had gone okay; I had been able to answer most of the questions and I wasn't as nervous as I thought I would be. The three people interviewing me, including Dave were really kind and were quite gentle with me. After my interview I went into the museum's café for a hot chocolate, I felt I needed a treat.

I sat in the café in my new navy dress and thought about the fun I had had with Mum the previous weekend when we had gone together to buy it. It had been a lovely weekend being back in the security of my family. Mum had looked really well and I think she enjoyed our trip into town as much as I did. We hadn't really talked about much while we were out, just general chit chat, normal mum and daughter stuff I suppose. I didn't ask her much about IT, deciding that I could draw my own conclusions by carefully watching her. She looked more tired than she used to do but also looked much better than the last time I had seen her. Mum had talked to me about when she was my age and how, in many ways, our lives were so different. Mum didn't get the opportunity to go to university, although I know she was academically very bright and would have managed the work really well. Instead she chose to get a job locally so that she could be near to the man she loved. I thought that was so lovely that she put aside all aspirations for a good career because of her love for the man who would become my father.

Mum talked to me about how she used to have such confidence and how she used that to her advantage when she was out with friends. Briefly I saw a flash of regret as she told me about how her girlfriends were all jealous of her good looks and all the boys envied Dad because he was going out with her. Unconsciously she ran her fingers through her hair and for a second a shadow crossed in front of her eyes. She quickly regained her composure and reached for my hand.

'Grab every opportunity you can my love, and don't let others stand in your way' with that she squeezed my hand and returned her attention to our shopping. I wondered what she meant *'don't let others stand in your way'* but it would only be much later in life that I would come to understand the relevance of her sound advice.

I felt quite grown up sitting there post interview. I wondered whether perhaps I would soon be on the other side of the counter as an employee. What an exciting thought that would be. As I drank my hot chocolate I thought about what I had achieved in the last year. I did well at Sixth Form and was really happy with my A Level results and managed to get into the university of my choice. The first term had been a bit rocky because of making the adjustments to living away from home and the safety of my family. But I had made some good friends and I had made it through to Christmas without really thinking that I would pack it all in and go home, even though once or twice I could have done quite easily.

I think I grew up a lot when I heard about Mum's illness. That had been such a shock, coming out of the blue as it did. The news had really knocked me and I felt a strong need to stay at home, to be close by to see what was happening and to do what I could. Of course, Mum and Dad were having none of it and insisted that I go back. I tried to convince them that I should stay, probably as much for my needs as theirs but my return to university was non-negotiable.

That was one of the worst journeys back to university. I was so sad and had an aching feeling in the pit of my stomach. I remember sitting on the crowded train feeling incredibly alone. It was a grey, cold January day that didn't seem to get properly light at all. The windows of the train were steamed up making it impossible to look out as the countryside flashed past. Not that I would have been able to see much anyway. The carriage was uncomfortably hot and airless; I was grateful that I had managed to get a seat as I would not have relished standing all the way back in that atmosphere.

My mind had been in a state of perpetual questioning. *Why my Mum?, why my family?, what was going to happen?, could the doctors have made a mistake?, why me just as I was starting my nearly adult life? What would I do if anything happened to mum? Why?*

Thoughts were racing through my mind about what was happening to my family. How could this come and spoil all that I knew and all that was safe. It all seemed so utterly unfair. We were just an ordinary family. Both Mum and Dad worked really hard and because of that had provided for us all a happy time and place to grow up. Mum was the kindest, most gentle person who never hurt anyone. She was always there ready to help out if needed and could always be relied upon to lend a hand.

We were, I suppose, what sociologists would call 'comfortable' and possibly even 'middle class' even though Dad was always vehemently denying this. There was a small mortgage outstanding on the house but apart from that I didn't think there were any financial worries. We always had plenty of good food, were always warm and had lots of treats. We didn't go on big holidays abroad; mainly because we tended to go to stay with Granny in her cottage or sometimes to Scotland to stay with one of Dad's aunts. I could remember when I was about fourteen having a big family discussion about going abroad on holiday. It seemed to me that all my friends were going to exciting sounding places abroad. They spoke about lying on the beach all day or swimming in the pool. It all sounded so good and I felt I was missing out so I broached the subject around Easter time. Mum and Dad listened to my carefully prepared, and what I thought rational, argument about why it would be good for us to go away that summer to Spain or somewhere else that was hot. I remember trying to wax lyrical about how lovely it would be for us all to have some 'proper weather' and for Daniel and Titch to be able to swim every day. I'm not sure how much of a compelling argument I presented but once I had finished we explored options. Dad pointed out that yes it might be nice to go away 'on a proper holiday' but also said that that would cost lots of money and it would mean that we would only get one holiday instead of the three or four we usually managed because of going to Granny's. So he gave me two options to think about, one big holiday abroad or our usual ones with Granny, playing on the beach and crabbing off the pier. Even to a headstrong teenager, Dad's argument made utter sense and so with that I put away all thoughts and desires of going abroad.

As the train continued its journey back towards my now second home, I thought back about growing up and realised that we had not really faced any big challenges as a family, or at least none that I were aware of. Apart from the usual colds and tummy bugs we had all been quite healthy and none of my really close family had died. I was very young when Grandad died and couldn't really remember him. I vaguely remembered one of Dad's cousins being diagnosed with cancer and dying but we didn't really know him. Dad was upset about it and went to the funeral but it didn't have an impact on our lives. But now we were facing the biggest crisis ever and I felt a coward because I was running away from it back to university. I should have been at home with Mum; she needed me to help her and to support her looking after Titch and Daniel. I wasn't sure what I could do in reality to help, but not being at home made me feel very inadequate. With every passing minute the train was taking me away from where I should be; it was a conspirator with IT in this awful crisis that was unfolding before our very eyes. The rhythmic rattling of the train became embedded in my head; the noise in tune with the words that were being repeated over and over in my mind *'why my Mum, why my Mum, why my Mum.'*

My new university friends were all full of talk about their Christmases and the parties they had been to and the old flames they had met up with in drunken liaisons. I didn't join in the conversations. I didn't want to share my precious memories of being at Granny's house and the lovely time we all had as a family. I didn't want to admit that I'd not been to any riotous parties and that I hadn't had any quick kisses with boys from school. But most of all I didn't want to share the pain and grief I felt when we got home and I learned about Mum's illness. I didn't think any of my friends would understand; it wasn't an easy conversation to start with people you didn't really know. And more importantly I didn't know how I would react with them. How would I respond to their questions? Would I just shrug my shoulders and pretend that everything was okay and that I was quite comfortable talking about my Mum, her illness and the fact that for the first time in my life I had to actually face the prospect of death.

The telephone call from Dave, the day after my interview, really lifted my spirits. I'd successfully navigated my first interview and now had a job with proper money, oh the excitement. Dave explained about the shifts and that he was aware that I was at university and so did not want my work to compromise my studies. He said that initially they would only give me two twilight shifts per week and one shift each weekend either on Saturdays or Sundays. He said that I would be working predominantly in the café. The museum shop closed at 4.45pm and so I might get some shifts there at weekends but more than likely I would be in the café. He asked me to attend a brief induction during the day and thankfully it was when I didn't have any lectures. He finished the phone call by saying that all three people on the interview panel had been impressed by my maturity and how I had answered the questions. He said they were all looking forward to me joining the team.

The induction went really well and everyone seemed very friendly and helpful. I was told all about the health and safety policies, food hygiene, customer service and how to operate the cash register which was all computerised. I'd never used a cash register before, apart from the one I had for Christmas when I was about five, but I didn't think that counted. I also had a lesson in operating the coffee machine, which was a bit scary as it had a tendency to splutter out boiling water in all directions.

Dave said that for the first few shifts I would be shadowing another member of the team called Dora. I briefly met Dora; she seemed quite nice and friendly. Lastly they gave me my name badge which they said I needed to wear at all times when on duty. When I got back to my room I took a photograph of the badge and emailed it to Dad. His reply was simply a smiley face.

I was nervous all day before my first shift. I can remember sitting in a lecture and finding it really hard to concentrate on what the lecturer was saying. Afterwards I went into the library for some self-directed study time but after reading a few pages of a journal article decided that I was wasting my time so went back to my room.

Once I got to the museum my nerves left me and I was okay. Dora was there to meet me.

'Hello Rebecca, are you ready for this?' she asked with a smile.

She went on to explain that Tuesday nights were generally quiet and so we should have a good shift for me to start to get to grips with the role. She told me that when there were events on in the evening the café would be really busy. She queried why the management bothered to open up when there were no events on but concluded that as long as they were paying her she didn't care whether we served anyone or not.

Dora was correct it was a quiet shift and so I had time to work out how to use the cash register and to get to know where everything was. Dora chatted away about her two children and how she had this job because it fitted in with school life. She said that her youngest child was only eighteen months old and she didn't want to leave him in day care. She stayed at home during the day and when her partner got home she then went out to work. She asked me lots of questions about my family and my home town. I decided not to tell her about Mum and IT so I just kept it all quite vague. I spoke mainly about Titch and how we missed each other.

* * *

I was amazed how quickly I got into a routine with the job and how I learned what I needed to do and when. Both Dora and Dave commented on how well I had fitted in to the new role and that they were both pleased with my work. I really enjoyed the job and after a few weeks asked Dave if I could have an extra shift. He was unable to give me a regular third evening but did promise that when possible he would.

As I got to know Dora better I found myself talking to her about Mum and IT. When I first told her it was because I was having a particularly bad day worrying about Mum. I knew that she had a hospital appointment and was worried about what she might be told. I always got nervous when I knew she was seeing the consultant, GP or nurse. Because of my shift I had not been able to telephone home to find out what had happened so I kept having sneaky looks at my phone to see if Dad had texted me. Dora noticed me and asked if I was expecting a text from my boyfriend. I wondered why people always made the assumption that if you were checking your mobile it was because you were waiting for a message from your boyfriend.

I felt it was only fair to explain why. 'Err no, I'm hoping my Dad is going to text me.' I said as I could feel my face going red with embarrassment, 'Mum's poorly and she was at the hospital today and so I just want to know how she has got on.'

'Oh love, I'm sorry that must be hard for you, how long has she been poorly?'

I found myself telling Dora everything, all about coming home from our Christmas holiday and me guessing that something was wrong. I told her about the treatment and how I was really worried about what was happening. Dora listened carefully, occasionally nodding her head to show that she understood what I was saying, but remaining quiet. When I had finished my story, Dora asked if, after work, I would like to go for a quick drink at the nearby pub. I didn't really want to, I wanted to get back to my room so that I could ring home but I felt obliged to say yes.

After we had finished tidying up the café and Dora had cashed up for the night we left the museum and set off to the pub. Thankfully it was quiet in there too; I guessed people were staying in because of the miserable, unseasonal weather. I had a coke and Dora ordered half a lager. Dora told me that when she was twelve her mum died after a short illness. She said that she could begin to understand a bit of what I was feeling and although we had different circumstances there were some similarities. She talked about feeling really uncomfortable talking to her friends about the illness and her mum at school and that she was for ever making up excuses so that they didn't visit the house and see her mum looking so ill. She asked me how much I knew about Mum's illness and whether Mum and Dad talked to me about what was happening. I told her that they were okay at sharing information with me but that sometimes I wondered whether they were telling me everything. Dora said she knew how that felt because her parents had tried to hide the illness from her. She said she knew that something was happening but wasn't sure what it was. She told me about when her mum became really ill and they knew that she was going to die. Dora said that she became really angry with her Mum and Dad because they had not told her how serious it was. That caused her to feel betrayed as she didn't get chance to say everything to her Mum that she had wanted to before she died.

Dora stopped suddenly 'oh love, sorry, here I am talking about my Mum dying. Your Mum will be fine, I am sure she will, you said yourself that they are doing everything they can to fight it. But I do kind of understand what you are feeling and if you want to talk to somebody you know where I am.'

I was grateful to Dora, it was kind of her to take the time to talk to me, and I did get the feeling she understood more about what I was going through than anybody else. I told her as much but then made my excuses and left. I said that I wanted to ring home and see how everything was. Dora left with me, as we were leaving the pub she put her arm on mine 'remember, you know where I am if you want to talk.' With that she set off for her house and family and I started walking back to my room.

As I walked the thought hit me that Mum might die. I suppose I'd tried hard to not think about that as a possibly, but listening to Dora made me think about what the future might bring.

As soon as I got back to my room I reached for my laptop and did something that I had promised myself I would not do. I did a search for IT to find out as much as I could about the condition, its treatments and the likelihood that Mum might die. I read the information quickly but instantly wished that I hadn't. It didn't make for happy reading.

TEN

Nathan

The bar was noisy following the rugby team's win over our close rivals. I managed to get a table with two seats while Ryan fought his way to the bar. The atmosphere was noisy but happy as everyone wanted to celebrate a great win. The windows were steamed up so it was difficult to make out what the weather was doing outside. During the match it had been drizzling and was cooler than normal for the time of year.

I sat looking round at the familiar faces of people I knew by sight from the club. There was cheerful banter going on all around me and the occasional striking up of the team's song. Ryan carefully edged his way forward clutching two pints of beer and two bags of crisps. I wondered whether I should really be there. Angela had been insistent that I should attend the match; reassuring me that she would be okay for a few hours, especially as her Mum was there to care for her. Her Mum staying with us was a double edged sword. In some respects I felt able to leave Angela more, reassured that there was someone there to care for her but equally I felt hugely guilty that I was abdicating my responsibilities to someone else. It was my job to care for my wife.

'Cheers' said Ryan as he put the beers on the table. Just as he leaned forward a great hulk of a prop-forward squeezed past and knocked his elbow causing him to spill some of the beer. Big Billy, as he was affectionately known, could be best described as a gentle giant whose spare time was often taken up doing fundraising events for local good causes. But to anyone who didn't know him he struck a foreboding figure. He was nearly as wide as he was tall and sported long hair that looked as though a good trim would not go amiss and a beard that would make Father Christmas's look paltry. Big Billy was notoriously clumsy and as he knocked Ryan's elbow, Ryan looked up to him.

'Billy, that's half my pint gone you clumsy bugger,' he said with humour.

Billy looked at Ryan, the spillage and then the barmaid 'Gloria love, top him up will you, I've done it again.'

Once Ryan's glass had been topped up I picked up my beer 'cheers' I said wryly, grateful that Ryan had not added *good health* to his salutations. I took a sip, the bitter taste hitting the back of my throat. I knew I shouldn't be there with Ryan. I should be getting home to Angela and my responsibilities.

After a few minutes of idle conversation about the game Ryan took a long glug of his beer and carefully put his glass down on the table. 'How's things at the moment?' he asked. I'd been waiting for the question and was expecting it but it took me aback. How should I answer such a weighted question? Should I be honest and say that things were not good or do I keep up the pretence that had become the mask of our family? Do I tell Ryan that I am absolutely terrified of IT and what the future holds, that I don't think I can manage anymore, that I am totally shattered and currently running on adrenalin and not much else, that I am not sleeping or eating and don't know whether I am coming or going?

'Oh okay thanks' I heard the coward in me saying, 'yes the treatment is going well and the doctors are really happy with how things are going.'

The words came out with such ease; I never knew that it would be so easy to lie to my best friend. Was I lying to Ryan or was I lying to myself? Was I trying to convince the inner voices in me that all was okay and that we were going to get through this relatively unscathed? Was I keeping up a front, just as the rest of us were, to protect our vulnerable and unstable family unit? Maybe if the outside world thought we are okay then we would be.

Ryan and I went back a long way. We became friends at secondary school. We both shared a dislike of education and it was evident that neither of us were going to reach any academic heights, much to the disappointment of our respective families. When I started to bunk off from school in the final year Ryan initially covered for me with our form teacher and my Mum. But gradually he too took to leaving after the register had been called. The geography of our school meant that it was really quite easy to slip away unnoticed. It was an old complex consisting of different buildings dating back to the Victorian era when it had been built as the Boy's School. To the rear of the school was the playing field which in places was not fenced off, making our escapes even easier. Running alongside the playing field was a public footpath that linked two main roads that ran parallel with each other into the centre of the town. The footpath was rough ground and generally overgrown with vegetation. It had small paths leading off which took you into the housing estate that had been built post war. The path was used by locals to access their homes and by gangs of school children when it was home time, or in our case when it was time to get out.

The two main buildings in the school, where most of the teaching took place were intersected with the staff car park and the bicycle sheds where some of the boys left their bikes. Ryan and I tended not to use this to make good our escape as it was overlooked by classrooms. And also once we had run down the public footpath we could easily head into town or across the bridge to the canal where we spent many an hour throwing stones and assorted rubbish into the already dirty water.

We remained friends when we had officially left school and I had started work with Uncle Bob. Unlike me, Ryan scraped through his GCSE's and secured an apprenticeship with a local engineering firm. Ryan was my best man at our wedding and with that our bachelor nights out ended. Not long after Angela and I married Ryan also gave up his bachelor status and married Tish who had been in the year above us at school.

Ryan glanced at me with a quizzical look. 'How's Angela doing?' he asked.

A fear stabbed into my chest, he knew that I was lying; he'd known me for too long, we'd been through too much together for him not to know. I reached for my pint. Having the glass in my hand formed a protective barrier between me and him. While ever that was there I felt that my exposed weaknesses were hidden from my friend. His questioning brought the old demons back into clear focus. They took me back to my eight year old self, standing by Dad's hospital bed, not really knowing what was happening but also being acutely aware that something bad had happened to our family and that things were about to change. I could hear Dad saying in his weak voice *'look after you Mum son, you are the man of the house now'*. The man of the house. I was really not doing a good job with that role now, I was allowing everything to fall apart in front of my eyes and I was being a passive bystander watching from the wings as my family imploded. I was letting Angela down, I was letting the children down, I was letting Dad down, I was letting myself down.

The pain and anguish of the last few months rose to the surface. I had been trying so hard to suppress all my feelings. While ever they were buried in the pit of my stomach they were safe but now in the middle of the rugby club bar they came to the surface.

'You know, good days and bad days, but on the whole she's okay, we all are.' I said, trying to fight the rising tide of emotions that were about to explode. I gulped down a swig of beer in the hope it would push the feelings back down where I had carefully managed to store them since I had first found Angela crying on the settee. So far I had been externally strong all the way through the diagnosis and treatments. Even when things have taken a steady decline I had stayed strong and optimistic on the outside. But inside every moment had felt like an eternity. Every visit to the hospital, every phone call, every glance towards Angela, all played out in super-slow motion as my life and my family's life hung in the balance because of IT.

I looked at Ryan and could see concern and compassion in his eyes. He didn't need to say anything; he knew enough to know what was happening. But he didn't know, nobody knew, how could they? People might try and say all the right words and offer help but they didn't know and at that moment I wasn't sure I knew either. I felt a prickle behind my eyes followed immediately with a lump in my throat and a pain in my heart that made me think it was going to explode. The tears started and no matter how hard I tried to stem them they carried on. I tried to stand to go to the sanctuary of the Gents but my legs wouldn't allow it, oh no son you can show your emotions to the world and show everyone that you have failed – you are not a man, how can you be a man with all those tears? How can you be a man when you are doing nothing to help your ill wife?

I began to sob uncontrollably into my beer. After the initial fear of self-exposure my masculine inhibitions left me. I didn't care if everyone in the bar was watching me. My life was in turmoil, the most precious thing in my life was fighting for her health and I was helpless. The pent up emotions of the last few months were finally being released. Ryan's kindness had been the trigger that finally allowed me to let go and expose my vulnerabilities to the world. But what was I really crying about? Was it IT that was the cause or my own vulnerabilities? I was sure that in part it was my feeling of anger towards IT along with the nagging frustration that I was powerless to do anything to stop IT in its tracks. I wanted, more than anything else for Angela to be better and for our family life to pick up where we had unceremoniously left it just after Christmas. I felt sure that if we could just get IT sorted we would be able to carry on, pick up the pieces and move forward. I suppose looking back to that particularly dark hour there were a host of factors making me feel as I did. But of course there was nobody there to tell me that at the time.

For a while I was oblivious of the world around me. I was caught up in my own emotions as the pain and anguish were released from my inner world. Ryan to his credit did not flinch. He sat watching me as a protective friend. He remained quiet but was alongside me with my pain. For that I would be eternally grateful to him. Later he told me that people made a hasty retreat from the tables near us, their embarrassment at my display obvious to see. I suppose it is a natural reaction of people; as a society we are very bad at dealing with serious illness and death and therefore prefer to ignore it. To compound it a male, in a rugby club sobbing makes a heady cocktail of embarrassment. Men don't cry and we don't talk about the possibility of death so instead we take our pints, remove ourselves from the situation and return to dissecting the game try by try. And in our trivial conversations of conversions and tackles we quietly thank our good fortune that it is some other family that is facing a crisis and not ours.

Following the sudden and violent release of my emotions a calmer distress came over me. 'Sorry mate' I sniffled to Ryan as I reached for a handkerchief to wipe my eyes. I made my excuses and this time managed to convince my legs that they could propel me to the relative refuge of the toilets. As I walked towards the Gents I felt that my every movement was being scrutinised by inquisitive eyes watching me. Were these people looking with sympathy, empathy, pity or embarrassment? Right then I didn't really care; I was too lost in my own emotions to care about anyone else.

In the toilet I ran the cold tap and splashed my face. I dried it the best I could with those rough green paper towels, every rub feeling like sandpaper on my face. I briefly felt thankful that the rugby club had not installed electric hand-dryers; now that would have been a challenge. I looked in the mirror but it was not my face that stared back. It was the face of a much older me, a face full of pain, sadness, guilt and anger. The face in the mirror was the face of despair and anguish. The face in the mirror epitomised the future me. There were few traces left of the old me, an empty shell where all my hopes, dreams and taken for granted life had ebbed away quietly, almost unnoticed until now.

I returned to Ryan who was still sitting at the table nursing his pint.

'Sorry mate, I think I ought to get off, look I'll give you a ring in a couple of days.'

'Hang on Nathan, are you sure you are okay to drive, let me take you and I'll pick my car up later.' Ryan looked anxious and helpless.

'It's okay thanks, I'll be okay, need a bit of time on my own before I go home. Say hello to Tish for me and the kids.' I made my cowardly exit, leaving Ryan looking helplessly into his beer.

I made my way to the car. The drizzle had now become persistent rain and the car park was awash with puddles. I reach into my pocket for my car keys but then with a shake of my head changed my mind. I pulled at the car door to check it was locked, stuffed my hands deep into my jacket pocket and set off walking. I needed time and space before I went home. I was in no fit state to go home immediately, I didn't want Angela to see me like this and also I had an overwhelming need to be alone. To be alone with my thoughts, fears and sadness.

As I set off to walk home my head felt as though it was going to explode. The emotions so wound up that my mind could not cope with all that I was feeling. But in a strange way I also felt nothing, I was numb and oblivious to all that was happening. The rain was insignificant, the dark April evening meant nothing; I was void of the ability to connect with my surroundings. I was on autopilot, a wet form of a homing pigeon, heading back to the place that generally represented safety but which was now the place that was harbouring pain and sadness. All I felt was an overwhelming sense of fear and emptiness. The omnipresent worries about Angela's health and the uncertainty about what would happen to IT were jostling for space in my mind with the Whitesnake lyrics *Crying in the Rain*. The words were playing on a cruel loop constantly repeating themselves. Never had the words of a song been so powerful and prophetic. It was clear to me that no one understood my heartache, no one felt my pain because no one wanted to see my tears as I was crying in the rain.

The streets were almost deserted, just a few dog walkers begrudgingly dragging their pets for their evening stretch. The rain was beating down now on man and beast with some determination. As I walked some of them looked up, briefly moving their heads from the relative warmth and dryness of their assorted raincoats to offer a nod. None spoke; maybe they too were lost in their own thoughts. Maybe when they glanced and saw the tears streaming down my face they, like the rugby fans, decided a nod was more than sufficient. Maybe like the words in the song they didn't want to see my tears as I was crying in the rain.

When I got home, Angela was still up, she looked anxious.

'Where have you been?' She asked as I walked through the door. I looked at her in a confused way. She knew where I was going, we had discussed it before I left.

'Ryan phoned half an hour ago to see if you were home, he sounded concerned about you. Are you okay?'

For the third time that night I was unable to control the wave of emotions. I held Angela close to me as I started to sob again.

'I'm so sorry my love, I'm so so very sorry' was all I could say.

Angela held me against her frail, ravaged body. She too started to weep quietly to herself.

ELEVEN

Titch

'Mum I don't feel very well I don't want to go to school today.'

Mum looked across the kitchen table at me. She still had her dressing gown on, the pink fluffy one that I helped Daddy choose last Christmas as her present. Her hair looked messy and all tangled up and she hadn't got her make-up on. She frowned and asked me what was wrong.

'My tummy hurts' I said 'and I feel sick.' I added.

Mum came over to me and put her hand on my forehead like she always did when we were poorly.

'Please Mum, I don't want to go today.' I said again.

Mum squatted down beside me. 'What's wrong Titch, why don't you want to go?' she got hold of my hand and started gently rubbing it with her thumb.

'My tummy hurts.' I repeated.

Mum sighed gently and said that maybe I should go back to bed. She said that she would telephone school and tell them that I was ill and wouldn't be going in.

'Come on' she said 'off to bed.'

I climbed back into my bed that was still warm from when I had got up a few minutes earlier. I snuggled under the pink flowery duvet cover. I could hear Mum speaking on the telephone and then heard her talking to someone else. I couldn't decide whether it was Granny or Dad, but I thought I had heard Dad go out earlier, before I was up.

I could hear Mum saying 'no she says she feels sick so I'm going to give her the benefit of the doubt today.'

There was some more muffled conversation that I couldn't quite hear then I heard Mum say 'I don't suppose she heard us last night; I thought they were both asleep when you came in.'

I didn't hear a reply but thought that Mum must be talking to Dad. He'd gone out last night to watch the rugby with Uncle Ryan. I knew that Granny hadn't been out because she gave me my bath and read me a story before I went to bed. She'd read me one of my favourite books from when I was little. I liked it when Granny read me a story.

I lay in bed listening but Mum and the other person had gone into the kitchen and closed the door. I liked school and I liked my teacher, Mrs Rigsby. She was kind and always had a smiley face. My favourite lessons were English and History and today I was missing both of them. Sally was my best friend at school and we always sat next to each other. Sally lived with her Mum over the newsagents shop near school. Her Mum and Dad didn't live together because he had got a new wife and a baby. Sally didn't see her Dad very much now that he had got the new baby. Sometimes she was really sad and so I would try and cheer her up. I liked going to her flat to play. Her Mum used to be a dancer and she always wore really pretty clothes that she had made. When I went to play with Sally we could sometimes look through her big pile of scraps of material. If Sally's Mum wasn't busy she would sometimes get her sewing machine out and let us have a go at making little bags and one day she helped me make a cushion.

I fell back to sleep and had a dream about going to Granny's house and all of us going to the beach for a picnic. It was a lovely warm summer's day but the beach was empty apart from us and a big dog in the distance. Dad was a Viking and he had gone into the sea in his boat and had sailed off without saying good-bye. I had stood in the water shouting to him to come back but I watched as his boat got smaller and smaller. Then the big dog had run along the beach and had pushed me into the water. It was cold and I began to cry because I was wet and frightened. All the time I could see the boat getting smaller and smaller.

I woke up and looked round my room. I wasn't at Granny's I was in my bedroom and there were no big dogs near the sea. 'Mum' I shouted, 'Mum.'

Mum came into my bedroom. She still had her dressing gown on and her hair was still messy and unwashed.

'What is it my sleepy head?' she asked as she sat down on my bed.

'I've had another dream about Dad going away again, he was in a boat on the beach at Granny's, he was a Viking and he sailed off without saying goodbye.'

Mum stroked my forehead 'oh Sweetie it was only a dream, don't worry Dad hasn't gone anywhere.'

Mum put her arms round me and gave me a big cuddle. She smiled at me but I could see she looked worried.

'It was only a dream' she repeated, 'it was only a nasty dream. Now then how is that poorly tummy?'

I wasn't sure how my tummy was, it felt all knotted up and tight as though someone had wriggled their hand into my tummy and was squeezing it. I didn't know what to tell Mum so I just shrugged my shoulders. My tummy hurt but now my head did as well because of the nasty dream.

'Where's Dad?' I asked.

Mum told me that he had had to go and see the team who were working for him. 'But' she said, 'he'll be back soon, he hasn't gone for long, so don't you worry my little Titch.'

'Mum, is Dad okay?'

Mum looked at me before she answered, I could tell she was thinking carefully what she was going to say. 'Yes of course he is, why?'

'I heard him come home last night when he had been to see Uncle Ryan and I heard him crying and then you started.' I decided not to mention that I had cried myself to sleep last night.

'Mum I know you are poorly, are you going to die?'

* * *

'Mum are you going to die?'

I'd been wanting to ask Mum that for ages but had been too scared because I knew that something was wrong but I didn't know what. Things seemed to change when we got home from Granny's house after Christmas. I can remember one day when we had just gone back to school and I came home at tea-time. Auntie Tracey was at our house and said that she was going to take me, Daniel and Rebecca to her house for a treat. Auntie Tracey was one of Mum's best friends; she lived quite close to us and sometimes as a special treat would invite us to her house. But that day it all seemed a bit strange. Usually when we went to her house it was on a Friday or Saturday and Mum and Dad came along too. But that day we left Mum at home. She said she wanted to talk to Daddy about something and that Auntie Tracey had offered to make us a special tea. When we got home later that night it looked like Mum and Dad had been crying. They both had got blotchy eyes and their noses looked red as well.

Rebecca had asked them what was wrong but they said that they were okay and that nothing was wrong. Even though it was a bit strange I didn't really think anything about it then, it was only later when I started to notice other things happening that I remembered about us going there for tea and it all being a bit different.

I had asked Rebecca what was happening before she went back to university, but she had told me to stop imagining things and that everything was okay. I really missed Rebecca when she went back and wished she would come home for the weekend like she did sometimes.

But then I started to see other things happening with Mum; one day I had walked into the hallway and heard her on the telephone to Granny. She was talking about the hospital but when she knew I was there she started talking about taking the car in for a service. As she saw me she looked cross that I had walked in. Just after that Granny came to stay with us. She said it was because she was missing us after our Christmas holiday and that she wanted a holiday but I wasn't sure she was telling the truth. But Granny always told the truth and always made us tell it too.

I knew Mum was poorly when she was off work and it wasn't the school holidays. She told me that she had an upset tummy and that it would soon be okay. She said that she had to go and see the doctor because he was making her tummy better. I was worried about Mum's tummy but because she had had days off from work before I wasn't too bothered. After a few days she went back to work and so it was all okay. But then after the Easter holidays she didn't go back to work and that made me scared again.

I was beginning to get scared that something was wrong. I kept thinking that Mum must be really really poorly and that she would have to go into hospital and have lots and lots of nasty operations and then she wouldn't come home again and we would all have to go and live with Granny. I was scared that Mummy didn't love me anymore and that was why she was poorly, then one day I thought that I must have made her poorly when I had been naughty because I hadn't put my toys away.

I kept thinking about having to go and live with Granny and having to leave all my friends and our house. Then I worried that Daddy wouldn't come to live with us at Granny's and that he would stay here and that I would never see him again. Then I thought that maybe Daddy didn't love me either.

When I had heard Mummy and Daddy crying last night I wondered if they were talking about me going to live with Granny and that they were sending me away because they couldn't look after me while Mummy was poorly.

I cried myself to sleep, holding on to Tootles my teddy bear. I knew that Tootles loved me, even though it felt as though nobody else did.

I didn't know whether I wanted to ask Mum but I knew nobody was going to tell me anything and so I had to ask her.

Mum looked really sad when I asked her if she was going to die. I thought she was going to cry and her voice went all wobbly but she didn't cry. Instead she took a big breath and then carefully thought about what she was going to say to me.

She asked me why I thought she was going to die. I told her that I had been watching and listening and could see that things had changed. I told her that I had seen that she had lost weight and that she didn't wear her make-up anymore. I said that I had heard her talking to Dad and Granny and Auntie Tracey and that I knew something horrible was happening.

Mum pulled me close to her and stroked my hair. She told me that of course she wasn't going to die but that she was a bit poorly but that the doctors were making her better. She didn't tell me much about IT but she did say that sometimes she did feel poorly. She said that was because of IT and also because of all the different tablets that the doctors were giving her to make her better.

She cuddled me and told me how much she loved me and that everything was going be okay. She said that she was sorry that I had heard her and Daddy the night before and said that she had been cross with Daddy for leaving the car at the rugby club and so they had had an argument. But she said that they were friends again now and I didn't need to worry.

Mum asked whether I thought some warm milk and a biscuit would make me feel better. I said that I thought it might so Mum went back to the kitchen and brought me some milk in my favourite mug with ballet dancers on it and a jammy dodger biscuit.

Because Mum had told me that everything was going to be okay I felt hungry and really enjoyed the biscuit and drink. After I had finished, Mum sat with me while I went back to sleep. I snuggled down under the duvet and this time dreamt of being a dancer like Sally's Mum used to be.

TWELVE

Angela

'Mum I know you are poorly, are you going to die?'

Titch's question was like a spear in my heart. When I had first been diagnosed with IT, Nathan and I had talked about what we should tell the children. Rebecca worked out very quickly that I was ill. She had confronted Nathan before she went back to university after the Christmas break. I had not wanted to tell her anything, I was worried enough about her going back and whether she would settle back into the routine of being away from home. Nathan and I had discussed it after the first appointment with the consultant. We had agreed that we wouldn't say anything to Rebecca until she had finished her exams. We agreed that we would go and visit her for the weekend after her exams and tell her then. However, her insistence when she had spoken to Nathan made it evident that she had guessed too much and Nathan had told her more of the truth than we had really wanted. I suppose he hadn't really got an option, he had to tell her.

I had been furious with Nathan when he told me about his conversation with Rebecca. We'd agreed that we would tell her together and that we were going to plan carefully what we were going to say and then he had told her. What would she think of me not telling her myself? She was a daddy's girl and there was no getting away from that. She had a much more positive relationship with Nathan than she did with me and this, I thought, would have just added to it. I had always felt that I needed to work additionally hard with my relationship with Rebecca. The early months when we should, according to the text books, have been bonding were lost because of my battle with depression. I knew that I did not give Rebecca as much attention as I should have and that at times I resented her for spoiling the life I had. But even through the really dark times I still nurtured her as any mother should. For a long time, when she was young, I beat myself up with guilt about how I had not given her the best start in life. I felt bad that my reticence to embrace motherhood had probably affected her development and affected our relationship. Throughout her growing years, friends tried to convince me that I had done an okay job mothering Rebecca and the other two. But I always had my doubts. Silly niggles that caused me to question our relationship. I felt guilt at spoiling her early childhood and with the arrival of IT felt guilty all over again. This time because I had spoilt her transition from child to adult.

I remember going into her bedroom after Nathan had given her the news. She looked at me with tears in her eyes, 'oh Mum' was all she could say before she started crying again. We held each other for a long time.

Through her tears she kept repeating that she could not go back to university and that she had to stay at home to look after me. I was in turmoil as I hugged her. A million thoughts racing through my mind. She was anxious about going back as she was still struggling with the transition to university life. She had been very homesick when she had first left home last September. It had eased a little as the weeks passed, especially after she had made friends with Cassie. Nathan and I had met Cassie when we went to stay with Rebecca for the weekend at the end of October. She seemed to be a really pleasant, level headed girl and I liked her instantly. She was studying psychology and so didn't attend lectures with Rebecca but they saw each other regularly when they hadn't got their heads stuck in books.

Before IT had come on the scene I had so wanted Rebecca to go back to university after the Christmas break with a new found confidence and optimism. She had done really well in the first semester and I was hopeful that we could nurture that so that she felt more positive about being there. But then this damned interruption had come into our lives. I struggled with what to do. Of course there had been no question about her going back to university, that was a given. But the emotions that I had felt all those years ago when I had left her at school for her first day came surging back. The guilt, the questioning of whether I was doing the right thing, the overwhelming feelings of loss. I wanted her to go back to university but I also needed all my family to be at home, to be in close proximity where I could see them, care for them, protect them from what was happening.

And so, very reluctantly I talked to Rebecca about the consultations with the GP and specialist. I told her as much as I dared without scaring her but also tempered the information thinking that she didn't need to know everything there and then. I didn't want to burden her with the compounded worry of my health and her being away from home. But partly also if I told her too much information I would be articulating out loud the fears and worries I had in my heart. If I told Rebecca too much I would be admitting that I was ill. I couldn't allow that to happen because it would be a sign of acceptance and acknowledgement. And in those early days of turmoil after the diagnosis I was not ready to acknowledge or accept that I could potentially be dying.

Mr Gough, the consultant, had looked uneasy when he had delivered the body-blow of news. I suppose it was an occupational hazard for him, the imparting of bad news and in fairness to him he had executed that bit of the consultation well. He had told us the facts in a very calm, professional manner and had quickly given a glimmer of hope when he spoke about the potential treatment and that he had seen other patients in similar circumstances who had been treated very successfully. That was the tasty filling in his sandwich of bad news because then came the next wave of bad news. Although he was optimistic he also felt it important to be open and honest with us. The results from the scan had not been as good as he had anticipated and so he wanted to be extra vigilant to ensure I was getting the best possible care.

As he spoke my first thoughts were the children. What was I going to tell them, how were they going to cope with such devastating news? I couldn't leave them, I couldn't die, who would look after them, who would be there for them? Nathan was a great dad but he couldn't possibly be a mum too. How would he manage Titch and her needs as she reached puberty, she needed a mum, she needed me. And what about Daniel, his hormones were already working overtime making him into a monosyllabic teenager who had temporarily lost the power to communicate. He needed me to referee his regular clashes with Nathan. Underneath his bravado he was still a young boy who was really quite sensitive and he wasn't ready to face the world without me as his comfort blanket. And Rebecca, what about her, she was just entering an exciting time in her life with countless opportunities ahead of her. She was an intelligent girl who, with the right support at university was going to forge a great career for herself. She was bubbly and had an infectious smile that endeared her to all who met her. She was also incredibly caring and thoughtful but with that there came a sense of her being vulnerable because of her sensitivity. One of my initial fears for Rebecca was about her being away from home and not knowing what was happening. In one sense that was a blessing; she would be able to bury herself in her work and have some distance from what was happening at home. But at the same time the not knowing was also going to play hard on her.

I remember the look of uncomfortableness on Mr Gough's face when I whispered *'what about my babies?'* I was conscious of the nurse sitting to the side of us also moving uncomfortably in her seat. Mr Gough cleared his throat as though he was going to speak but instead he looked at his computer screen. He glanced at the nurse and as he did I too looked to her for some support. *'Come on woman'* I thought, *'you must be able to begin to know what it feels like to be in this situation, you must have some answers'*. She too stayed silent and offered a glance back to Mr Gough. This exchange had bought him a few seconds and in that time he appeared to have regained his professional composure.

'Err, I realise this is an awful shock for you Mrs Williamson, I would like to see you in Clinic next week so that we can discuss the best treatment. I would like to speak to my colleague about this before we proceed. If you have any questions please ring my secretary on this number.'

With that he offered his hand which clearly signalled the end of the consultation. As Nathan and I stood to leave, he told me to try not to worry and said that the nurse would give me information about the Clinic appointment. Nathan and I dutifully left his small room. We were both in a state of shock. I reached for Nathan's hand as he steered me out of the hospital and away from the epicentre of bad news. As we walked through the main entrance I thought back to how I had felt less than an hour earlier when we had walked in through the same revolving door. In the back of my mind I had known it was not going to be good news, but I had hoped that I was being overly dramatic and that I had worked myself up into some emotional frenzy that would soon be dispelled. Now I wondered how many times the revolving door had gone round in the last hour. How many other people had gone through it with all their hopes dashed.

The cold January air caught our breath as we walked away from the hospital. Neither of us could face going home and so we went for a walk through the local park. Despite all the council cuts they still managed to keep the green spaces looking tidy and well tendered. We walked alongside neatly clipped grass which was dotted with trees. They stood like sentinels, dark and brooding against the pale blue winter sunshine. Their bare branches reaching out into the cold sky. It was too early for any sign of buds or new growth but I knew that it would be only a matter of time before they would explode back into life as the cycle of life progressed. Would I be like a tree I wondered? Would I burst back into life after the crippling news from Mr Gough?

A crow high up in the branches started cawing as we walked underneath the tree. I was not generally superstitious but seeing and hearing it added to the desperate place I was in. I remembered the conversations Dad and I used to have when we were walking through the

Norfolk countryside when I was a girl. Dad was a great storyteller and would tell me stories of wildlife and about the animals in their natural habitats. One of his stories that I particularly remembered was when we were walking through the woods near our cottage. It was a Sunday morning in November, Mum was at home preparing lunch and Dad and I had taken Chalkie out for a walk. I was about six and was very excited because I had been bought a new pair of red wellingtons the previous day when we had been into Norwich on the train. All Saturday night I had wanted to go out in my new treasures but had to make do with wearing them in the cottage. I remember the excitement when I saw that the Sunday morning was dry and bright.

Dad and I set off with the breeze stirring the branches of the mighty oaks and beeches which stood majestically along the tree-lined path into the woods. I whooped with delight as I rustled my way through the fallen and now crisp dry leaves. The percussive sound of them noisily breaking the silence. Dad smiled as he whistled a tune quietly to himself. As we got deeper into the woods Dad started telling me one of his stories. It was about a family of crows who lived in the very wood that we were walking through. It was a long rambling story that sparked my imagination and offered just enough suspense to provide an element of fear and anticipation. Within the story Dad told me about the crows and why they had the collective noun 'a murder of crows'. I was enthralled as his story unfolded and he added snippets to the plot that related to the different bits of nature that we saw and heard.

The sight of the crow took me back to the six year old me and that November day all those years ago. Now there I was walking with the other man in my life feeling wretchedly sad, scared and angry. Nathan and I sat on a bench; he put his arm round me and pulled me close to him. I could feel the roughness of his hands, roughened through years of working with them and yet also so tender and soft. We had been silent up to this point. Both of us lost in our own thoughts and emotions. I kept replaying Mr Gough's words silently in my head. Maybe he was wrong, doctors make mistakes, you hear about it all the time in the news. Maybe he had muddled up my notes and it was another Angela Williamson who was really in this position. Tomorrow the hospital would realise their mistake and make a frantic and apologetic telephone call. I played out the phone call in my mind, the relief and anger in equal measure as Nathan and I cried with joy.

But then Mr Gough's voice returned to dominate my thoughts. No this wasn't an awful mix up, it was me he was talking about, and it was my life he had just released the wrecking ball on to.

'What are we going to do?' I asked Nathan. I spoke quietly and carefully as though I was choosing each word for maximum impact.

'I don't know love, I really don't know.' was his honest reply.

'I'm sorry' I said 'I'm really so very sorry.'

Nathan pulled me closer to him and kissed the top of my head.

'We need to make a plan' he said, 'we need to think this one through carefully, we can manage it, we can do this together.'

I briefly felt reassured by his confidence. Since we had married I had always relied on Nathan. When we had faced problems I always knew he would sort them. When I had depression after Rebecca was born, he had been the strong one for me; he had managed everything and had got me through those dark days. Nathan was blessed with a very methodical, logical brain. His thinking and planning was always rooted in a calculated well thought through manner which I admired so much and which I had come to rely on. His considered approach generally found solutions to problems.

I looked into his blue eyes and wondered whether this time he would really be able to sort it. How could he? If the doctors were unsure then how could my hero? My mind was racing in every direction but I kept coming back to the children; what was I going to do? How could I let them down? They needed me, I needed them, I needed to be there for them. What, oh what was I going to do?

'What are we going to say to the children?' Nathan's question broke our silence. 'I think they are too young to know and besides, we don't know all the facts yet so there is no point telling them anything.'

I mumbled that I agreed with him but then followed that up with my anxieties about not telling them. 'They know that there are no secrets in our family that is how we've brought them up, we can't start to lie to them now. They are going to find out sooner or later, what about if I have to go into hospital for treatment?'

Nathan shook his head, 'no, it's too soon, there's no point upsetting them.'

I turned my head away from him to listen to the wind stirring the trees into life. I felt torn between thinking what was best for our children and what was right. I didn't want to tell them about IT; how does a parent begin to have such a conversation with their children? What on earth would I say? Would I have the emotional strength to cope with their reactions? What words would I use *'hello kids,*

Mum has got some news for you' No I couldn't begin to think about such a conversation. Anyway, Nathan was quite right, we didn't know the full facts yet and so it was best to keep quiet and not tell them. No they didn't need to know.

And all the time I was thinking those thoughts the mother in me knew that I really did not want to have to tell my babies this. They did not need to hear this.

On the park bench, Nathan and I made a pact, we would tell Rebecca part of the information after her exams in February. We would go over for the weekend and on the Saturday morning take her for a walk and tell her. We also agreed that we wouldn't say anything to Daniel and Titch. We'd tell them later on, maybe in a few months when we had started to get used to the idea ourselves and once we had a better idea of how long it would be before I was cured. With that decision being made I felt a crumb of comfort. I was aware that Nathan and I were going to have to acclimatise ourselves to the news. There were going to be so many things that we needed to sort out but if we didn't have to worry about the children that would be one challenge I could temporarily ignore.

No they would be okay not knowing. They were very young and it was too much of a burden to put on them. While we could we would carry on as normal, they would be okay. They would be okay.

I had misgivings about telling Rebecca, but I also knew that as she had worked out that something was wrong she did need to know. If she hadn't been told, I could imagine that she would have fretted and become very anxious being away from us. I suspected she would have started to weave her own story about what was happening. However, her version would potentially be filled with inaccuracies and would have become the stuff of imagination. At least by her knowing, as hard as it was, she had facts to work with not made-up notions. Nathan and I were very careful to spend as much time as she wanted talking about IT and the possible treatment options. We were aware that we needed to get this right because once she was back at university opportunities would be limited.

I had faced some challenging conversations in my life, like when I had to pluck up courage to tell Mum and Dad that Nathan and I were going out together. I could still remember the fear I felt as I waited for the right time to tell them. We had been going out together for about three months and I really knew that he was the one. But I also knew that Mum and Dad were not going to approve of him because he did not fit in with their plans for me. He had left school with no qualifications, had long hair and a particular liking for very loud rock music. In his favour he was the most gentle person I had ever met, and I knew I loved him. However, I was also acutely aware that my parent's first opinion would be that he was some rough boy who was not good enough for their daughter.

I had to endure a few battles before they began to see beyond the hair, biker jacket and torn jeans. But once they got to know him for who he really was their opinions quickly changed. Helped in part by his gallant gesture of undying love when he had his precious locks cut and arrived at our house with a very smart haircut.

But the conversation I knew I had to have following Titch's question was going to be the toughest yet. I felt like a cornered animal, I had no escape route and so for damage limitation decided that I should tell her the partial truth. Her questioning eyes searched mine as she waited for an answer. I remember pulling her close to me and stroking her hair. I was trying to control my breathing but was conscious that my heart was pounding in my chest. I didn't want Titch to feel this as I held her. *'Breathe'* I said over and over again to myself *'deep breaths, you can do this.'*

I tried to reassure Titch that I was not going to die and that yes her observations were correct and that I was poorly but that it was nothing that the doctors could not make better. I then lied about the previous night, telling her that I had been cross with Nathan for leaving the car at the rugby club and walking home in the rain. I couldn't possibly have told her the truth that actually her Daddy had been distraught because of IT.

I couldn't tell my baby that her Mum and Dad were absolutely petrified about what was happening and felt completely out of control. I couldn't tell her that my biggest fear was that she was correct in her questioning and that yes I probably was going to die much sooner than I had planned.

I think her young, trusting mind was satisfied with the reply and that for a while at least I had managed to stave off any anxieties for her. After drinking a cup of warm milk she fell back into a more restful sleep. I sat on her bed for a while watching her. She looked to be dreaming but this time I guessed it was a happy dream as she looked so peaceful. I thought about the innocence of childhood and the moral duty I had as a parent to protect my daughter from all harm. And yet there I was clearly not protecting her; because of IT I was putting her through enormous stress. For a brief period I might have bought us some time but I knew that it would only be a matter of time before the stark reality of this crisis was going to have to be faced by all of us. What kind of emotional stress would that put on Titch? She had a feisty nature and, from her playground adventures, could clearly stand up for herself but how would she manage this time bomb?

I thought back to when Rebecca was Titch's age and all the ups and downs we went through as she was growing up. The transition into secondary school and the new identity of being at 'big school'. The dreaded puberty and all that that brought; the tears and tantrums, the sulking and mood swings. The loss of the ability to communicate rationally with us and the changing relationships with friends. We had coped quite well with all that and Rebecca, to her credit, had navigated her hormones with relative ease. But how was Titch going to cope with all that without me being there to support and guide her?

Not for the first time a great cloud of anxiety hung heavily over me. And as the cloud loomed menacingly another thought struck me. Rebecca knew some of the facts and now I had been partially honest with Titch, two down one to go. It was time to talk to Daniel.

THIRTEEN

Angela's Mum

Driving to and from Angela's was becoming more and more difficult. As I was getting older driving was becoming less enjoyable. I'd stopped, wherever possible driving at night and tried to avoid going on motorways too. I wondered how much longer I would feel able to drive. But I also knew that once I stopped I would lose the independence that I enjoyed, and with the situation with Angela I had to force myself to carry on.

As I set off for home, the prospect of the long drive coupled with worries about Angela and the family weighed heavily on me. I'd been at Angela's for nearly two weeks and although I didn't want to leave her I was aware that being there was not always helpful. Initially Daniel and Kitty (I couldn't bring myself to call my youngest grandchild Titch, it just didn't seem right), saw my visits as additional holidays but I think as time went on they realised that there was more to it than me just being there for a break. I also knew that Angela and Nathan needed time on their own to try and work out some routines for them and the children. So reluctantly I set off south; leaving behind my daughter and her family to try and manage IT.

I felt very unsettled when I got home. Thankfully the journey had been a good one. I had deliberately set off early and because it was a Sunday there wasn't as much traffic on the road. So I was back home by lunch time. I telephoned Angela to let her know I was safe but then could not settle to do anything. I wandered round the cottage watering the houseplants and tidying away my things but I had a compelling urge to be outside.

On impulse I drove to the local seaside town and headed to the promenade for a walk. I thought back to Boxing Day when we had all walked along there. Kitty had been desperate to try out her new bike. I remembered how she had wanted to ride it on Christmas Day but the weather had been too wet. The following day had been much calmer and drier and so with great excitement we had all set off to the sea. It had been a lovely walk. There had been other families out too walking off their Christmas lunches and lots of good humour was exchanged with them. Inevitably I had bumped into some friends and had stopped to catch up with news. Nathan had teased me about knowing everyone and not being able to take me anywhere without seeing someone I knew.

We had laughed about it, but as I started walking along the prom I really hoped that I would not see anyone I knew. I wanted to be lost in my own world and didn't feel like making small talk for the sake of it. There were too many thoughts swimming around in my mind, too many things that I needed to think about and try and work out.

It was a bright afternoon but the wind was strong and was whipping the sea up into an angry frenzy. The tide was coming in, each wave crashing against the rocks with great force. A handful of children were standing on one of the jetties playing dare with the waves. They screamed with happiness as the sea got closer and closer to them, running backwards up the jetty to avoid getting soaked. They looked so carefree and happy enjoying such simple games. I wondered whether my grandchildren would ever find pleasure again in simple activities. Would they ever feel able to be themselves again?

I had observed dramatic changes in both of them. They were both very different children from the ones I had watched walking, cycling and running along this prom just a few months earlier.

Kitty had asked the question every parent must dread and with it had been brought into the family drama of IT. How must Angela have felt when Kitty asked her if she was going to die? No mother should have to answer that kind of question from her six year old. Kitty of course had guessed that something was wrong long before she had overheard Angela and Nathan talking after the incident at the rugby club. She had observed the changes that were going on around her and she knew that something serious was happening.

Following the diagnosis, Angela and Nathan had decided not to tell anyone, other than immediate family and friends, about IT. Angela's work, and by default Daniel's school, knew of course because of her being signed off. But they thought it was best not to tell Kitty's school about IT. However, they quickly realised that they had to tell the staff because of the changes in Kitty's behaviour. Her teacher had noticed her daydreaming and in a world of her own where she would stare into space. Also at other times she had got into arguments with one of her classmates and had then got into trouble. Apparently this happened a few times where my placid granddaughter changed into an angry little thing. On one occasion she hit one of the boys in her class; her anger at him so apparent that she marked his arm. Her teacher had intervened and had quickly de-escalated the situation. The teacher spoke to Angela about this. Initially Angela did not disclose the possible reasons but eventually saw sense and spoke to the head teacher. Thankfully, following that meeting, the teachers were made aware of the situation at home and were able to give Kitty additional support when she needed it.

Daniel too was showing signs that at times he was struggling. He tried hard to keep up a front but I could tell that he was finding it very hard to cope with all that was happening. His still saw his friend Joe but the rest of his friends were noticeable by their absence. Whereas in the past he would go out playing football with them he seemed to be staying in more. I wondered whether that was his choice or whether they had started to distance themselves from him. I couldn't decide whether the changes were because of IT or whether they were just typical behaviour of fourteen year olds.

I carried on walking along the sea-front. The churning of the sea, as it hit the rocks reminded me of a cappuccino. The sea looked coffee coloured and the white spray on top added to the frothy coffee picture. I briefly stopped to watch the force of the sea as it made its relentless impact on the rocks. I could feel the energy in it, the pent up emotions that it conveyed in its endless journey. As I stood quietly watching, transfixed by the sight, I felt I was the sea. I too had so many emotions rattling round in my mind. I was angry, of course I was angry. Why should my daughter be going through all that she was? Why was my family being tested to the limits? But also I felt helpless, frustrated and in turmoil.

My thoughts moved from the children to Angela and Nathan. While staying with them I had noticed changes in their relationship. Friends called them "the perfect couple" because of their love for each other. Their marriage was a true partnership built on trust, love and respect. To the outside world that may still have appeared to be the case, but I could see changes. They were more irritable with each other and their gentle banter was used less often. I could sense more tension between them, which I suppose was understandable but it didn't feel right. That damned IT was getting between them and that worried me so much. I could see that they were both trying really hard to be themselves but the worries of the illness were getting in the way. When I had asked Angela about how things were with her and Nathan she said everything was 'fine'. But as she said it a shadow fell across her eyes. I didn't know what to do. Should I have asked more questions, but was it really my place? Was that the kind of conversation a daughter would want to have with her mother?

I looked back at the sea and the horizon. I watched the off-shore windfarm as it rhythmically turned in the wind. I stood for a few minutes watching the movement. It was calming to stand and watch. Briefly my mind was free of worries. Briefly, amidst the crashing of the waves, I felt calm and at peace. But deep in my heart, I knew that was just a temporary feeling of respite that would disappear again as soon as it had arrived.

FOURTEEN

Daniel

Mum's illness had a big impact on me, not that I wanted to tell anybody that. I sort of guessed that something was wrong just after Christmas and so it wasn't a big surprise when Mum and Dad told me that she was ill. I can remember them sitting me down and saying that they had got something to tell me. At first I did wonder whether they were going to say that they were splitting up. I didn't know why I thought that really, probably because a lot of my friends' parents had recently got divorced. But I think I knew that that would not be the case. I knew how much they loved each other.

When they told me about IT, I think I was in shock and denial. My Mum couldn't get poorly, she was always healthy and very fit, and she took pride in her appearance and that included being very careful about her weight and what she ate. She didn't smoke and didn't drink loads of alcohol, not like Joe's mum. Joe was my friend from school and he was always talking about how much wine his mum drank every weekend. It seemed to be her badge of honour about how much more she had each weekend. But my Mum was different, she and Dad had the occasional drink, but I'd never seen them get drunk. Mum did get a bit tipsy one Christmas and she was really funny and made me and Rebecca laugh at her silly dancing, but that was all.

I didn't get angry at first when I heard about IT. I was too stunned and was trying to work out in my mind what it all meant. I think at first I just tried to carry on as normal. I still went to football on a Saturday morning and still met up with my friends after school on Fridays, but after a while that stopped. I didn't tell any of my friends about Mum, I decided that they didn't need to know, and anyway, I didn't know what to say to them. I remember missing Rebecca even more when she had gone back to university after the Christmas holiday. I thought that if she was at home, I would have somebody to share it all with. I knew that Titch was too young and also Mum and Dad told me that they hadn't told her all the truth about IT.

I did try and talk to Dad one day but he got upset and changed the subject so I decided it wasn't a good idea to talk to him. By then Mum was having her treatment which was making her additionally tired and so I didn't feel it was right to talk to her either. I decided that the best thing to do was to carry on as normal and to pretend that everything was okay.

But everything wasn't okay. I could see that Mum was getting more ill and that the treatment didn't seem to be working. I watched her very closely to see what clues I could get from her. I saw that her lovely bright skin had lost its glow and that she stopped wearing her make up. I saw that she was signed off from work and that that made her feel even worse. I heard her talking to Auntie Elspeth on the telephone one day. She didn't know I was standing at the top of the stairs and so could hear her side of the conversation. I heard her say something about feeling really depressed as she felt that she was useless because she couldn't go to work. She then said something about losing her identity. I don't know what Auntie Elspeth said to her but I think it made her cry. I saw that Granny was coming to stay more often. At first that was quite nice because it was usually fun when Granny was around, but after a while it started to grate with me. She started trying to tell me what to do and would tell me off for things I did. I resented Granny trying to parent me; that was Mum and Dad's job and I wasn't overly impressed with them trying, let alone Granny.

But then it got to the point where I couldn't carry on as normal and pretend that everything was okay. I started to notice that Mum and Dad were having more arguments. Usually silly, petty things, generally about money. Mum and Dad didn't, as a rule, argue. They sometimes disagreed about something but had always talked about it and sorted it out. But sometimes now they would shout at each other and not talk for a few days. That was really uncomfortable for me and Titch because we were so unused to it. Then one day, they had a massive argument about Dad not working. He had been taking more and more time off from work to look after Mum and to manage things around the house. Most of the time it had been okay because he had got some good contractors but when they let him down on a big job, he was in an awful mood. Him and Mum started rowing about it and didn't care who heard. They were shouting and saying horrible things about each other. I was in the room with Titch and kept turning the volume on the television up and up in the hope that she would not hear them. I don't think it worked because she got upset and started to cry. At that point I went into the kitchen and told them both to "shut up" because they were upsetting Titch. They both looked shocked when I shouted at them but it stopped them. Mum ran into the room to Titch and I made a quick exit because I didn't want an argument with Dad.

After that I knew that things were getting really serious. I asked Dad what was happening with Mum. He told me that, at that time, the treatment wasn't working as much as they had hoped. But he didn't say anymore, instead he told me not to worry as it would all be okay.

'Don't worry', that was a laugh, how could I not worry when I knew that something was wrong? I could see that things were getting worse. Titch stopped having her friends round to play because Mum couldn't cope with the extra noise and mess that they made. And also I think Titch was a bit embarrassed about having her friends round because they would all just stare at Mum, almost as though she was some kind of freak. Sometimes when I asked Dad for money to go to the football, he would make an excuse about not having had time to go to the cash-machine and so he hadn't got any spare money for me. That meant I could not go and meet my mates, and instead, I had to stop in.

It all came to a head when Mum was suddenly admitted to hospital. She had been feeling extra unwell; she was dizzy and had a really bad headache. Dad telephoned the GP who came to see her and he immediately rang for an ambulance. That really scared me. Me and Titch had to go and stay with Auntie Tracey for the night. Under normal circumstances it would have been good fun, but that night it wasn't fun. It was very scary and was a major turning point for me. I had to try and be grown up for Titch because she was really worried about what was happening to Mum, and she wasn't used to being away from Mum and Dad at night. So there was I telling her it would all be okay and that it "was nothing to worry about", but at the same time, I was really bothered myself. Thankfully on that occasion Mum was only in for one night, although she had to keep going back to the hospital for more treatment. But it had scared me and I didn't know what to do. I was scared about what was happening then but I was also scared about the future and what was to come.

The next day I went to school but found it really hard to concentrate. I kept thinking about Mum and what was happening to her. Dad had telephoned Auntie Tracey from the hospital to say that they were still there and to ask her to get us both to school. He had said that Mum was "okay" but hadn't said anything else.

What did he mean by 'okay'? Why did they always tell me that Mum was 'okay'? It didn't mean anything and it didn't tell me anything.

I remember sitting in my geography lesson and I started to fall asleep. To try and keep awake, I looked out of the window and counted how many trees I could see – I never knew there were so many near our school. My teacher, Miss Smith, saw me and asked if I would be kind enough to re-join the class. The rest of the class started laughing and I could feel myself going red. I mumbled my apologies and tried to look as though I was listening to what she was saying. But of course, I wasn't really listening about the rock structure of the Grand Canyon. I didn't care what kind of rock it was; all I could think about was watching the ambulance take Mum away the night before, and the worried look on hers and Dad's faces. I could see the blue lights disappearing into the distance, taking my Mum away from me.

'Daniel Williamson', I could vaguely hear Miss Smith's high pitched voice calling my name. 'Daniel Williamson', this time louder, 'I've just asked you a question, now if you would kindly tell the class the rock structures in the Grand Canyon.'

Her shouting brought me back into the class; I looked round and saw all my classmates looking at me. At the front of the class Miss Smith was standing, her arms folded across her chest. She looked red in the face with anger.

'Well?' was all she asked.

I looked back at her and tried to work out my options. I thought that I could be honest with her and say that I hadn't got a clue about the answer because I hadn't been listening as I was too worried about my Mum being taken into hospital. Or I could just walk out of class.

I chose the latter; scraping my chair on the wooden floor as I pushed it away from my desk. I calmly picked up my bag, swung it over my shoulder and walked past her.

'Daniel, Daniel' she shouted after me, 'don't you dare walk out of my lesson.'

I ignored her, my heart beating so fast I could hear it banging in my head. I wanted to shout at her, I wanted to say that her teaching style would better suit the teaching of chimpanzees in the zoo, but then thought that would be cruel to the intelligence of chimpanzees. Instead I carried on walking, increasing my pace with every step. I could sense that she was watching me as I made my way down the long corridor. I felt her eyes piercing my back. In the distance there was the sound of my classmates shuffling in their seats. I wondered what they made of my actions. I guessed probably shock because this was so out of character for me, but in a weird way, it felt so liberating. In one act of defiance I had released the chains of conformity that had seemingly been my companions for my whole life. I had finally tested the boundaries further than I ever had before. And at that moment it felt good.

I walked away from school but then a thought struck me; what was I going to do now? I couldn't go home, even though home was where I wanted to be. I didn't know what was happening with Mum and whether she was back home or still in hospital. If she was home she would have been so upset and angry with me for walking out of school, and I knew that I must not upset her. I decided that my best option was to go into town and then think about what to do next. I headed for the small café in the bus station. It was a dark, uninviting place, but the drinks were cheap. I reasoned that none of Mum and Dad's friends would go there for a drink, and so hopefully, I would not be seen by anyone who might incriminate me and my actions.

I ordered a mug of coffee and sat near the counter. I noticed how the paint on the walls was peeling off and that the tiled floor was stained with what looked to be the remains of yesterday's crumbs scattered all around it. On a table near me was a pile of newspapers. I saw from the headlines on the top one that they were a few days old. I read the headline, "Celeb Snaps in Drunken Brawl", and wondered why that should make the front page of the paper. Why did people care about stupid TV stars when good people were so poorly?

The air was heavy with the smell of bacon cooking. But not the appetising smell like when Mum cooked bacon for our Saturday morning treat, more a greasy, fatty smell. I so missed those old Saturday mornings, Saturday mornings were very different now.

There was one other customer in when I arrived, an old man with the biggest beard I had ever seen. I couldn't stop looking at him until he noticed me, stared back, and then muttered something under his breath. Then I felt uncomfortable and wondered why I was there and not listening to Miss Smith dribbling on about rocks. As I sat looking sadly into my mug of coffee two youths walked into the café. I guessed they were regulars with the way they spoke to the young waitress. They knew her name and she brought them two mugs of coffee without them making an order. I think they were probably in their late teens. They both had jeans on and tee-shirts. They sat by the window and looked deep in conversation. At one point I noticed them both look towards me but I managed not to give them eye contact. I felt really conspicuous in my school uniform. It was obvious that I was truanting from school, why else would I be sitting in a dark, dreary café on my own making a mug of coffee last as long as possible?

After what seemed an age, I decided that I couldn't sit there any longer. Reluctantly I left the relative safety of my hide-away and went back out into the street. I walked aimlessly round the town, trying to avoid places where I might be recognised by anyone who knew me or my family. I briefly went into the library, but it was full of overly happy parents and young children, all singing nursery rhymes and playing home-made musical instruments. So much for it being quiet I thought to myself. I pretended to look at the books in the Sports Section but thought that the librarian was looking at me. I decided that she must have known that I was not a legitimate library user so I made a quick exit.

Sometimes I had day-dreamed about what it would be like to bunk off school. I had a romantic image in my mind that it would be full of excitement and that I would brashly walk around looking grown-up and confident. But now in reality it felt really horrible. I was lonely, didn't know where to go, and on top of everything I was worried sick about Mum. I wondered whether I should try and telephone Rebecca and ask her advice, but then I thought she would say I was stupid for walking out of school.

In the early afternoon I decided it would be safe to go home. As I walked through the town back towards our house, I noticed the two teenagers who had been in the café. They were now standing outside the chip shop chatting to two girls. I don't think they saw me as I hurried by.

When I got home the house was empty, I made a sandwich and got changed out of my school uniform. I'd not been in long when I heard a taxi pull up outside our house. Dad and Mum got out from the taxi and came into the house. Dad was carefully supporting Mum with his arm.

'Daniel, what are you doing here?' they both asked together.

How do I answer that one I wondered? I didn't really want to say that I had not been able to concentrate in class, got told off by Miss Smith and then bunked off. I didn't think that would go down very well. So instead, I said that one of the teachers was off sick and our form had been sent home early. Suddenly lying was becoming too easy.

'How are you Mum, what happened?'

'Later Daniel' said Dad, 'let me get your Mum into bed.'

And with that he helped her upstairs. I could hear Mum in the bathroom, and then the floor boards in their bedroom squeak. After a few minutes Dad came back down stairs.

'She's resting' he said. I looked at him for an answer.

'Just a mini scare, nothing to worry about, but they have warned us that she might have more.'

'So what do you mean by a mini scare?' I asked, 'and how often is she going to have them, can't they do anything about it?'

Dad looked tired and I guessed he had not slept all night. I decided it was not the right time to push him for an answer. I knew that he wasn't going to give me the answer that I really wanted anyway, so I changed the subject.

'Cup of tea?' I asked.

Dad nodded a weary nod. I went into the kitchen and made us both a drink, but when I returned to the room Dad was on the settee, fast asleep.

* * *

I was dreading going back into school the following day. How could I face my teachers and my friends? What on earth was I going to say to my form teacher, who I knew by now would have been told of my behaviour? I'd never been in real trouble before at school. Sometimes I'd been told off in class for larking about with my friends, but that had generally resulted in a mild telling off; nothing on the scale that I was expecting. I was worried about going back but I was also still angry with Miss Smith. I knew I would have to apologise to her, but I really didn't want to. I wasn't sorry that I walked out of her boring class, I wasn't sorry for my behaviour. She didn't care about me or about what was happening to my family. I was pretty sure everyone in school would have known about IT because of Mum working in school. But it hadn't been spoken about to me and nobody seemed to remember what was happening.

I slowly and reluctantly started walking to school; I could again feel my heart beating as I got nearer. As I turned into the road where school was, two of the boys from my class walked past me.

As they overtook me they sang out 'Williamson, you're in trouuuble! Williamson you're in trouuuble!'

They emphasised the word trouble which made me feel worse. The bigger of the two caught my shoulder and pushed me off balance.

'Teacher's pet is going to get it' they mocked as they carried on their way, laughing together as they went.

I froze, the fear of being in trouble making me even more worried about going in. It was at that moment that I made the most stupid decision; I turned round and headed back into town. I was in a blind panic and clearly wasn't thinking straight.

I headed back to the café at the bus station and ordered a mug of coffee. I sat at the same seat and tried to make myself as small as possible. I wanted to cry but managed to stop myself. What had I done? There really was no going back now. All I could hear was the two boys taunting me, their cruel words ringing in my ears. Did people see me as being the teacher's pet I wondered? I knew some of them didn't like it because I kept my head down and worked hard. They were the ones who didn't care about getting into trouble. They didn't seem to think that there would be a life after school and that they needed to work hard for their futures. I think there was some resentment too because of Mum working at school. They saw her, and by default me, as one of them, the enemy. Some of them had passed snide remarks before about my family 'hobnobbing' with the head teacher. Their comments were an attempt at being humorous in front of their friends. It struck me that nobody in my class had mentioned that Mum was off sick. I wondered whether they had even noticed that she wasn't there, or was it simply that they didn't care.

As I sat in the café trying to work out what to do next, the two teenagers who had been in the previous day came in again. They spotted me and I could see one nudge the other. They got their drinks but instead of sitting at the table by the window, they hovered near my table.

'Hello Kiddo, in here again?' they asked.

My heart sank as they spoke to me. I dutifully nodded but tried not to give them eye contact.

'Mind if we join you?' the older of the two asked, as he sat down at my table.

Again, I meekly nodded my agreement to their request.

The older of the two sat across the table from me while his friend pulled a chair from another table and sat diagonally to the table, in effect blocking my exit. I could feel fear rising from the pit of my stomach.

'Not in school again? We are making a bit of a habit of this aren't we?' the older one said. 'Twice in two days, it must be serious.'

I had no idea how to respond. The older one took a sloppy drink from his mug, the contents spilling down his unshaven chin and dropping to the table. He casually wiped his chin with the back of his hand. I saw he had a massive tattoo on his hand. It was difficult to make out what it was but it looked like a tightly bound spider's web with writing in between some of the lines.

'Let me guess' he said, 'you've been a naughty boy and can't face going back into school, am I right Kiddo?'

How did he know that? Was it so obvious that this was alien to me? Did I stick out so much? I gave him the briefest of eye contact and nodded.

'Well, well, well' he muttered, 'what are we going to do with you?'

I could feel them both staring at me.

I shifted uncomfortably in my seat. I felt hot and scared, but also in a strange way, quite excited. The thought of being fitted into the category of 'rebel' had a bit of an appeal. That was an identity that was not generally associated with me. But then there were lots of identities at that time that were not generally associated with me. I didn't normally associate myself with being the son of an ill mother. I didn't normally feel as though I was being excluded by my family; but as IT took hold, I was beginning to feel more and more isolated and alone. I didn't normally feel angry, but the more I thought about IT, the more angry I became. I was angry that IT had changed my Mum, my family and me. We didn't do the same things anymore, and the only conversations I ever heard were about IT. I knew that Mum and Dad were trying really hard to carry on as normal, but our normal had gone. It wasn't normal for your Mum to be so ill and to be rushed into hospital. It wasn't normal that different professionals kept coming to the house. It was not normal that sometimes I thought that Mum might actually die, and then what?

'So, what are your plans, you can't sit here all day.'

I mumbled something about not knowing what I was going to do.

'You can come and have some fun with us if you like' said the older one as he nodded towards the younger one with a knowing grin. 'I'm Spider' he said, 'and this is Johnny' he said looking towards his friend.

I didn't know how to answer him; I couldn't make an excuse about going somewhere when it was obvious that I was not intending to go to the one place where I should be. I also knew that he was right; I couldn't sit in the café all day either.

So I found myself walking through town with two teenagers who I'd never met before. We headed out into one of the estates. The houses must have been built at the same time as ours. They all looked the same, a uniform neatness about them. I suspected that, like our estate, most of the people who lived in those houses were out at work during the day. They were what Dad called 'ant houses' because everyone went off to work in the mornings and then came back in the evenings.

I got the feeling they knew what they were looking for, and I was right.

'Bingo' said Spider as he spotted an old looking black Vauxhall Corsa parked on the road. My heart sank as I suddenly guessed what he was planning.

'Fancy a ride?' he asked.

Before I could comment, he had used his elbow to smash the back passenger window in; I stood transfixed as I watched him deftly start the car. The adrenalin was making my heart beat so fast I thought it might explode. I knew this was so wrong, but it also felt so exciting.

'Come on, we don't want to be here too long' he shouted with some urgency.

The tone of his voice jolted me into action. I climbed in the back of the car, trying to avoid the shards of glass that littered the back seat. Spider drove off at speed, recklessly driving over the speed bumps that were a feature of the estate's roads. As he drove, he and Johnny started laughing and shouting at each other. Johnny had a bottle of beer in his hand. He kept taking drinks from it as the car sped away.

For a while I think they were oblivious that I was in the back of the car. We were quickly out of the town and driving along the country lanes near to where our house was. The car got faster and faster and as it did I could feel the sense of excitement and fear rising in me in equal measure. The feeling of speed making me heady; I grabbed the edge of the car seat with my fingers.

The last time I had felt such scary excitement was when we were at a theme park for the day. Dad dared me to go on one of the big white knuckle rides. It was the first time I had been tall enough to be allowed on the big rides, and Dad bet me that I daren't go on. I could remember us both queuing up, waiting patiently for our turn. As the queue snaked round the barriers I began to feel a mixture of anticipated excitement and fear. But it was too late, I couldn't say to Dad that I didn't want to go on the ride, and so I braved it out. We both laughed as it slowly started to climb away from the ground gradually getting higher and higher. I briefly looked down and could just make out Mum, Rebecca and Titch, all straining their necks upwards as they waved at us frantically. As we climbed they got smaller and smaller, becoming three little dots on the grass near the entrance to the ride. Our laughter stopped when we reached the first of the corkscrew bends and we plummeted back towards the ground, twisting and turning as we did. I screamed and grabbed hold of Dad. As the ride went on I got braver and enjoyed myself, but was glad when it stopped and we both, very shakily, walked back to Mum, Rebecca and Titch. Dad looked quite pale when we met back up with the rest of the family. Mum teased him about not being the big brave Nathan that he thought he was. But I'd done it, I'd won the bet, and in the process had enjoyed my first (and last) time on a white knuckle ride.

The same feelings came back to me as I sat in the car. But this time the fear and adrenalin were masking the pain about Mum and IT and everything else that was happening in my family. It suddenly didn't matter that I was being ignored and that no one was talking to me about what was happening. I felt strangely calm and in control. Spider and Johnny still ignored me, but that was fine. I was happy to be in my own world where I was emotionally free from the worries of home.

We drove round for what seemed like forever, but in reality was probably only half an hour. Spider turned in his seat to look at me 'what do you think Kiddo, is this better that being at school?'

The car eventually stopped on some old industrial wasteland. Spider and Johnny got out and stretched. I noticed that they left the engine running and briefly wondered why.

'Come on, you can't stop here all day. So what's your name and what is it with school?'

'Err, Daniel' I said shyly 'trouble with a teacher yesterday so I walked out.'

It struck me that it was only the previous day when I had walked out of Miss Smith's class, yet it seemed like it was ages ago.

'Bitch' was Spider's observation, and with that he turned his attention to a rolled up cigarette that Johnny had given him. He had a long drag on it and then passed it to me. I had no idea what to do with it, I'd never smoked, nobody in my family smoked and it always seemed to me to be a horrible habit. I took the cigarette from him, desperately trying to look as though I knew what I was doing. I put the cigarette in my mouth and took as small a breath in as I dared. The smoke caught the back of my throat and I started coughing violently. I passed the cigarette back to Spider as I struggled to breathe. I thought I was going to be sick with coughing as I tried to control the feeling of chocking. As I bent over coughing I noticed, out of the corner of my eye, the two boys look at each other and then back at me.

They knew that all this was alien to me; they knew that I didn't fit in with this kind of life-style. They saw me for what I was, a frightened wimp who couldn't do anything.

The derelict remains of the factory were eerily quiet, not even the birds were singing. Spider broke the uncomfortable silence that surrounded us.

'Don't think you are ready for all this are you Danny-Boy' he said, 'Mummy wouldn't be happy if she knew her little boy had just nicked a car and was smoking dope with two wasters. What would she say?'

'Leave my Mum out of this' I said, trying to sound braver than I was feeling 'leave her out of it. My Mum is ill, not that it's got anything to do with you.' I heard myself shouting at him.

For a brief moment I felt some compassion from Spider. A shadow fell across his eyes 'sorry that must be crap for you.' He stubbed the rolled up cigarette into the ground with a determined twist of his foot and then indicated to his mate.

They went back towards the car; I dutifully followed and climbed in the back of the car, feeling a sense of relief that we were back in the vehicle. This time Johnny got into the driver's seat. He set off at speed, causing the dust and grit to spin up behind us. We were heading back the same way we came, but this time I reckoned we were going much faster. As the car sped down the country roads I began to feel more and more frightened. The potential repercussions of my actions slowly beginning to hit me.

I suddenly thought about one of the Sixth Form boys from my school. Last year he had stolen a neighbour's car for a bet with his friends, but it had all gone horribly wrong. He'd started to drive it down the road near us known locally as the 'Straight Mile' but lost control on some mud on the road, went into a skid and hit a tree. At the inquest the Coroner said that he would have died instantly. The tragedy hit the community hard, the neighbours blamed the boy's parents and there was real animosity between them. I heard that the boy's family moved away, not being able to cope with the pain of losing their son and then the hostility from the neighbours. The story was all over the papers and the police came into school to talk to us about the dangers of 'irresponsible behaviour'.

As I sat in the back of the car, I kept hearing the policeman talking to us about the repercussions of stealing cars and joy-riding. I suddenly thought that the term joy-riding didn't fit. I certainly wasn't feeling any joy.

About a mile away from town, the car suddenly stopped.

'Time to walk now Danny-Boy' said Spider 'if ever you fancy some more fun, you know where to find us' he said with a sarcastic laugh.

I pulled myself from the back of the car and looked at the two youths.

I didn't say anything to them. I just stood in the layby as they drove off, again spinning the wheels of the car as they went. For a while I could still hear the sound of the engine but then a strange silence fell around me.

FIFTEEN

Daniel

As I stood in the layby I wondered what on earth I was going to do. I reached for my phone to check the time. I then noticed that I had six missed calls from Dad. My heart sank; had something happened to Mum and was she back in hospital? Or had school telephoned home to say I wasn't there? With fear rising from the pit of my stomach, I wondered what I should do. I desperately wanted to ring Dad and find out what had happened, but I also knew that if I did ring him, I would be in massive trouble.

I stood for a while trying to think about what I should do. I suppose I knew that at some point I was going to have to go home and face the biggest telling off of my life, but was so frightened to face it. Suddenly being in a stolen car that was being recklessly driven by two strangers felt a good option. I was cold, hungry, tired and alone, and didn't know what to do. I slowly and reluctantly started walking in the direction of home. The road didn't have a pavement which made the walk back slow going; I kept having to stand aside to let the cars and lorries go past; their speed causing a draught as they went.

The long walk back into town gave me time to think about what I had done. I knew I had been stupid. I shouldn't have walked away from class but the anger I had felt at Miss Smith, and at everything else, had erupted inside me and nothing could have stopped that. I tried to think logically about what was happening:

Mum was ill.

Nobody seemed to be telling me anything of any real substance – they just told me what they thought I needed to know without asking me what I needed and wanted to know.

My family was not the same family I knew before Christmas. Everything had altered, even though we were all pretending that it was all the same.

I was scared about what was happening and about what was going to happen in the future.

School didn't care.

Miss Smith didn't care.

Nobody cared.

As I was making my mental list, I noticed a police car driving towards me. The driver slowed down as he went by and looked at me. A horrible thought struck me, did he know about me bunking off school? Had the owners of the car reported it stolen and now the police were out looking for me and the other two? The policeman drove on. I let out a huge sigh of relief and quickened my pace. I needed to get home as quickly as possible. I hadn't gone much further when I was conscious of a car coming up behind me. I could hear it slowing down as it got close to me. *'Don't look'* I told myself, *'just carry on walking.'* The car pulled up alongside me. It was the police car again.

'Excuse me son, can I have a word with you?'

I looked into the police car but didn't say anything.

'Are you okay?' asked the policeman 'why aren't you in school and what are you doing so far away from school?'

I still didn't say anything, partly because I was too scared to speak, but also because I didn't know what to say.

'Come on, you can't be walking down here on your own, get in.'

For the second time that day, I climbed into a car with a stranger. The policeman set off driving back towards town. He asked me my name, why I was not in school, and why I was walking down a country road on my own.

I told him my name and said that I had bunked off from school because I had had an argument with my friends. I thought it was a bit of the truth.

'We've all done it' he said 'so where is home, I need to talk to your parents, will they be in?'

I gave him our address and said that I thought Mum would be at home. I didn't give him any more information. I'd never been in a police car before, apart from when I was about seven and the police came to our school. Then I had sat in the driver's seat and the policeman had let me wear his helmet. I felt strangely safe as I sat there being driven home. I knew I was going to be in big trouble with Mum and Dad, and now, potentially the police as well. But that didn't seem to matter.

As we were driving back towards home the policeman spoke on his radio to the station. He told them that he had just picked up a Daniel Williamson and gave our address. I heard him ask if they could do a check on us. I didn't hear the answer but hoped that there was nothing to report. He asked me which school I attended and said that luckily for me, it was so late in the afternoon that he would be taking me home and not back to school.

The policeman made general conversation about school and problems with bullies, but on the whole, the journey home was in silence. When we got home I could see that Dad's van and car were on the drive. My heart sank because I knew he must be home.

Mum and Dad must have seen the police car pull up because before we had got to the door they had opened it.

'Mrs Williamson?' asked the policeman.

Mum nodded to confirm who she was.

'I've just found Daniel out for a ramble, he says he has bunked off from school, can I come in please?'

The policeman and I walked through to the living room. Neither Mum nor Dad said anything, but I could see that they were both really angry and worried at the same time.

'Does Daniel make a habit of wandering the streets when he should be in school?' asked the policeman.

Dad said that I didn't and that this was very out of character of me. Thankfully he didn't say anything to me, but the look he gave me seemed to say 'once this policeman has gone, you'd better have a very good reason for not being in school.'

'I'm really sorry about this Officer; school telephoned us earlier to alert us to the fact that Daniel was missing. I'm not going to make excuses for him because he is clearly out of order, but at the moment we are all going through additional stress. Angela, Daniel's Mum, is ill and it is taking a toll on all of us.'

The policeman looked over to Mum. 'Sorry to hear that Mrs Williamson.'

Dad shuffled uncomfortably, 'Err, do you think we can deal with this Officer?'

The policeman looked at me and then over to Dad. 'I think under the circumstances, this time yes. However, I will need to inform school that I have picked Daniel up.' Then he looked at me. 'But Daniel, if I find you wandering the streets again, I might not be as lenient.'

Dad thanked the policeman for bringing me home safely and saw him out. I heard Dad say that he was really sorry for the bother I had caused, and that it would not happen again. I looked out the window as the policeman walked back to his car.

Dad came back into the room. Mum looked at him, but spoke to me.

'Where the hell have you been, what have you done?' She shouted. 'We've been worried sick.'

I looked across at Mum. She looked tired and worried, but also relieved. I still didn't know how much they knew about school and guessed that they didn't know about the car and the two lads. I wondered what I should tell them. But as I stood there I knew that there was no point trying to weave anymore stories. For the past day, I'd been lying to Mum, Dad and me. All it had done was get me into deep trouble.

'I've been stupid' was all I could say 'sorry Mum, I've let you down.'

'We know about school Daniel, what we don't know is why.'

'I got into trouble yesterday in geography for not concentrating; I was thinking about you and what had happened when you were taken into hospital. I wasn't interested in rocks and the Grand Canyon, all I could think about was what was happening to you.'

I stopped and looked at Mum and Dad. I could see Dad was still really angry with me but Mum just looked tired and very sad.

'I walked out when Miss Smith started on at me about not concentrating and so I went into town. I really did plan to go back into school today, but on the way in, Neil and Kyle started picking on me, saying I was going to be in big trouble. I knew I was in trouble, but when they started, it just freaked me out so I went back into town.'

I stopped talking and looked down at the carpet.

'Oh Daniel' was Mum's only comment.

'And then what?' asked Dad; he clearly knew there was more to this than me just hanging around town until now, and he clearly knew that worse was to come.

I moved uncomfortably on the spot, and cleared my throat. 'I went off with two older boys.'

'Go on and?' said Dad.

'Err, they got a car and we drove round for a bit.'

Dad was now bright red with anger

'YOU DID WHAT?' he asked very slowly and carefully, using the full power of his voice.

I guessed I didn't need to spell out that we had stolen the car and that I was party to a crime.

At that point I stupidly burst into tears.

'I'm sorry, I'm really sorry' was all I could say through my sobs. Mum came and put her arm round me. She led me to the settee and sat down beside me.

She let me cry for a while and then gently said 'so what is all this about Daniel? This is so out of character for you, what's wrong?'

What's wrong? I thought she would have known the answer to that one. I looked at her, she looked older than she ever had before, her eyes were tired and her skin had very little colour.

'I panicked when Miss Smith shouted at me' was the best answer I could find.

The silence seemed to last forever. I was struggling with my emotions. I wanted to be able to feel like a small, innocent five year old again where it is okay to cry and people didn't see it as a weakness. But I also felt I had to be strong and act the part of a cocky fourteen year old, because that is what they did on the TV and in films.

'I'm sorry.'

Mum and Dad looked at each other and sighed; it was Mum who broke their silence.

'No Daniel it is me who should be sorry, sorry that IT has made everything so damned impossible. You wouldn't have behaved like this if it wasn't for the illness, I know that.'

She looked back over to Dad for some assistance; I could sense her eyes pleading with him to say something helpful and supportive.

Dad cleared his throat, 'well, have you learnt anything from this?' He asked.

I wanted to say that I had learnt that my parents were unable to share difficult things with me, and that I now understood how crap growing up was. I wanted to say that I had learnt that clearly I wasn't so important in our family life that I didn't need to be included in things, even when they were painful. But I didn't. Instead I said that I had been stupid but that I was still angry with Miss Smith. I reckoned it was easier to blame her than IT and Mum and Dad's behaviour towards me.

'You do know that you will have to go and see her and apologise don't you?' said Mum.

I nodded a very reluctant nod.

'Nathan, put the kettle on for us will you please love?'

Dad disappeared into the kitchen, I could hear him filling the kettle and getting the mugs from the cupboard. While he was out, Mum got hold of my hand.

'I know this is difficult for you Daniel, I'll try my best to help you, I promise.'

I wondered what she meant by '*I know it is difficult.*' Did she mean that I had been a complete idiot getting involved with those lads? Or that she actually knew that I too was struggling with IT. I knew that it was Mum who was ill, but IT was affecting me just as much.

SIXTEEN

Nathan

I could sense Daniel's anxieties as we got into the car. His Mum and I had agreed that it should be me who took him back into school after his run in with Miss Smith. Angela warned me that Miss Smith had the reputation of not being the most compassionate of teachers in the school. That knowledge and also her concerns about going into her workplace when off sick being her rationale for asking me to see the head teacher and possibly Miss Smith.

I understood Daniel's apprehension, I too felt nervous about facing the head teacher, but not because of my son's misdemeanours but memories from when I used to be hauled in to see my head teacher all those years ago. I glanced at Daniel, *'that's my boy'* I thought to myself.

When school had alerted us that he was missing, Angela and I were frantic with worry. It was so out of character for him to do anything like that. School failed to tell us about the incident with Miss Smith which annoyed me very much. They were happy to telephone and say that Daniel was truanting but didn't seem to consider why that might be. Apparently the two bullies from his class had told the form teacher that they had seen Daniel heading into town instead of into school. At least in my day when I bunked off my mates covered for me.

When he came home and told us about what he had done, Angela and I took the decision to keep him off school the following day which was a Friday. We reckoned that it wouldn't do any harm for him to have some distance between what had happened and returning and thankfully the weekend gave us the break we needed. We were all emotionally drained that weekend, what with Angela being admitted to hospital and then all the trouble with Daniel, it was good just to have some time as a family to catch our respective breaths and attempt to re-gain some normality.

On Saturday after lunch Daniel and I went for a walk. Angela thought it might be a good idea to have some 'man time' together and so off we went to the local county park. The park was a good place to go as a family. There were wide, level paths that circumnavigated the man-made lake. The paths were perfect for younger children to practice riding their bikes and scooters on. It was a regular haunt of ours and, when they were younger, Rebecca and Daniel had enjoyed riding their bikes there. The lake attracted a lot of wildlife, especially geese, ducks and swans, but in the summer there were also regular sightings of swallows and swifts.

Daniel seemed glad to be out of the house, the park gave him a sense of freedom from the constraints of the four walls of home. Angela and I had decided not to ground him for his behaviour. We both recognised that he was gutted by his actions and that he had been sufficiently scared by what had happened not to require any further sanctions from us. However, we did notice that he opted to stay close to home and not venture far.

We walked in silence for some way, just briefly commenting about the different birds feeding on the lake. I think we were both lost in our own thoughts. I was thinking what I could and should have done differently to support Daniel. I should have seen this coming, and should have recognised how vulnerable he was with everything. I was angry with myself for letting him down. If I'd not been so wrapped up in Angela's health and my own fears and anxieties I might have seen the signs. If I'd just spent some more time with him, just silly things like going for a walk maybe he wouldn't have felt so isolated and ignored. Maybe I should have done more about his school being better informed. I had wrongly presumed that because Angela was off sick they would have known that Daniel might be being affected by IT. If only I'd spoken to them and made them aware that he might not be able to concentrate as much as usual or that he might have a blip with his school work.

After my initial anger at Daniel for bunking off from school like that I calmed down and realised why he had done it and how troubled he must have been to do it. Then I was angry with myself; further evidence of not living up to my old man's expectations of me being the man of the house.

It was Daniel who broke the silence, 'Dad, is it okay to be scared?'

I glanced sideways to look at him, 'you'll be okay, we'll go into school together and I will talk to the Head, don't worry, we'll sort it.'

Daniel nodded but then became quiet again; he looked out towards the lake but I could tell he was not really looking at the view. His mind was elsewhere. We walked on in silence but this time it felt uncomfortable.

After a few minutes Daniel looked at me; he opened his mouth as though he was going to say something but stopped himself. Instead he kicked a big stone that was lying on the path. The force of the kick shocked me. Daniel watched the stone as it rolled along the path, 'why don't you just listen' he shouted at me and with that started running. The anger within him giving him added speed.

I shouted after him but it was useless, he wasn't listening. I knew it was pointless trying to chase after him; he was far fitter than me and I didn't have the energy any more to even try and compete with my fourteen year old.

I carried on walking round the lake, again feeling that I had let Daniel down. But what had I said? He asked me if it was okay to feel scared and I had replied that we would sort school out, what was the big deal. God, right then I could have done without a hormonal teenager, I'd got enough to cope with thinking about Angela and our future. What was the big issue about school anyway, we've all bunked off in our time. Daniel you are not the only one who is bloody scared at the moment; I'm out of my mind with worry about your Mum.

Then it hit me with the force of a steam train going at full speed. I groaned to myself, of course it wasn't school that Daniel was worried about, it was Angela and everything that was happening. Oh shit, why did I not see that one? There I was thinking about all that had happened over the last few days and had completely missed the point. Yes the teacher's reaction had been the trigger but all that was happening with Angela was clearly having a bigger impact on him than I had guessed. Maybe I'd just been blind to the fact, wrapped up in my own worries and fears.

I continued walking round the lake but could not see Daniel. I arrived back at the car park and spotted him sitting on a wooden log. He looked so vulnerable and sad; it took me all my effort not to start crying but I knew that that would not have been helpful. I walked up to him 'can I join you?' I asked.

Daniel nodded so I sat next to him on the log. 'Sorry son, I've been a complete prat haven't I?' I said without looking at him. We both sat staring in front of us.

'I think I can guess what is scaring you but tell me so that I know for sure. Is it about Mum?'

Daniel looked at me, searching my eyes for some answers.

'I'm scared about what is happening to Mum and to all of us. You keep telling me bits but I don't know whether you are always telling me everything about what is going on.'

Daniel stopped talking and an uneasy silence fell between us.

It was true, we had told Daniel and Titch as much as we thought they needed to know, but now I began to realise that our over protection had backfired. Since we had first given the children some information about IT Daniel had been the quiet one. He'd not said much and not really asked many questions. Angela and I assumed that he was just getting on with it and that he was comfortable with the amount of information he had got.

Hindsight is an amazing thing and with it I could see that through our well-intended approach we had caused him massive internal unease. Not only had he been coping with all the angst a fourteen year old boy has to cope with he had the added burden of worrying about his Mum. I groaned to myself. Bollocks.

'Come on, let's go for a drive' was all I could think of to say.

We drove out into the countryside, me being mindful not to head out the way the youths had done the other day when they had taken Daniel. We stopped at a disused railway line that was now used as a public footpath and cycle path.

'Quick walk to the tunnel and then we'll head home' I suggested.

When the children were younger the walk to the tunnel had been a regular Sunday afternoon outing. The children loved running into it and making as much noise as possible; listening to their voices reverberating off the walls. It always made me smile how Titch was the bravest of the three and would fearlessly run into the dark cavern without a second thought. I wondered whether she was maybe the one that was coping the best now, or was I blind to her needs too.

Daniel and I walked along the path where the old track would have been.

'How much do you want to know about IT?' I asked Daniel.

Driving to the railway line had bought me some thinking time which had been really good. In those few minutes I had decided that I needed to take the lead from Daniel and let him tell me what he wanted to know. I figured out that his questions would show how much he needed to know and how much he thought he could cope with knowing.

'I don't know' was his answer 'I just need to know that you are not keeping stuff away from me. Like the other day when Mum was taken into hospital, I needed to know what had been said and what they were going to do about it but instead you just ignored me. I sometimes feel like you are treating me like a child and I'm not. I can see what is happening and I know that things aren't as good as you two make out. This is a big thing for our family and I want to be part of it.'

* * *

'Are you ready for this?' I asked as we parked the car near to the school. I didn't wait for an answer; instead I said 'just remember we've all bunked off in our time.'

Daniel looked at me with a quizzical look.

'Yes son, I was the world's worst, not that your Granma ever found out. Just about the only certificate I got from school was the one for the most times absent.' I joked.

Daniel grinned at me; I think I had just gone up in his estimation.

'Really?' he asked.

'Yep, star pupil at that one, and even worse I encouraged Uncle Ryan to join me too. I'll tell you all about it later; come on lets go and be nice to the Head.'

We sat outside the head teacher's office waiting to be suitably reprimanded. I think I was more nervous by this time than Daniel. I looked down the corridor and wondered how many children and parents had sat in the same seats over the years. How many I wondered had been hauled before the Head because of similar misdemeanours by children struggling to cope with some family crisis or another. I wondered how much these issues were taken into account within school policies, were they noted as being worthy of recognition? Somehow I doubted they were, even in today's society the emphasis remained on educational achievement and not social and emotional needs. I smiled to myself, if only my old man could have heard my thoughts, he would have been proud of me.

The Head called us in and invited us to take a seat. He sat behind his substantial oak desk. I wondered whether the power of his position made him feel superior to me. I didn't suppose he would have approved of my antics when I was at secondary school. Oh the shame.

He gave a long spiel about respect in class and that Daniel's behaviour had been unacceptable, made worse by his previous good record of attendance and attainment. He said that as a school they took this kind of behaviour really seriously and that he needed to consider carefully what sanctions he would give to Daniel. I wriggled uncomfortably in my seat but let him finish.

He looked at Daniel over his glasses, 'well Daniel do you have anything to say for yourself?'

Daniel looked towards the floor and remained silent. Before the head teacher had chance to speak I asked if I could pass comment.

'I assume you are aware that Daniel's mother is seriously ill?' I said, trying to sound confident and not intimidated by the Head.

'We are all under a lot of strain at the moment, and the illness is affecting all of us. Daniel is trying hard to cope with his school work and I think on the whole is managing this very well. However, last week's incident was triggered because his Mum had been admitted into hospital the previous night as an emergency. The boy was tired from a restless night worrying about his Mum and was finding it hard to concentrate in class because of the continuing concerns about her wellbeing. I agree that his behaviour was wrong, he should not have walked out of class and I do not condone his actions, but I also think that under the circumstances he had some justified grounds for his behaviour.'

I'd not planned a speech and was quite pleased with my defence of my son. Again I thought Dad would be proud of me, I was clearly being the man of the house now.

The Head looked at me; I think my opening sentence had reminded him about Angela and the fact that one of his team was off work ill. I tried hard to remember whether he had signed the get well card which had arrived with a massive bunch of flowers.

'How is err Angela?' He enquired, faltering to retrieve her name from his memory.

'At the moment she is in a difficult period, the treatment isn't going as smoothly as we would have hoped but we remain hopeful' was my reply.

Did he really care I wondered.

'I'm sure it must be a difficult time for all of you. Now Daniel do you have anything further to add to your father's eloquent explanation?'

I gave Daniel a cursory glance, willing him to say he was sorry. Daniel must have read my mind.

'I'm sorry' he half whispered, 'I know I shouldn't have done it but I was so worried about Mum.'

'You should have said something to Miss Smith or your form teacher, I am sure they would have understood.'

'Maybe there needs to be some kind of system in place so that teachers can be alerted to any issues without the children having to expose their emotions and issues in front of their class.' I suggested, thinking that my suggestion would be a helpful way forward.

However, the Head did not respond and instead suggested to Daniel that he and the Head should go to see Miss Smith so that Daniel could resume classes immediately.

The Head looked at me 'I do hope Mrs Williamson is better soon; please send her my best wishes. I hope that Daniel can try and maintain his previously excellent attitude to his school work.'

I could feel the anger, that I had tried to hide, rising in me. So that was it, clearly the Head's priority was that the children in his care were all model pupils whose behaviour did not disrupt the smooth running of the school. But what about all the children who were in similar situations to Daniel? I'd never really thought about such circumstances before but I guessed that there were many Daniel's in the school struggling because of family circumstances.

'I'm sorry' I heard my self saying, 'but you seem to be missing the point here, my son is struggling because his mum is seriously ill and all you seem to be bothered about is him behaving and not disrupting the class. I think you have some responsibility here for what has happened. Don't go blaming Daniel when clearly if he had some proper support from you lot he might just be able to cope a bit better.'

My voice was getting louder and louder and I was conscious that I was beginning to lose control. But my anger at the way the Head had spoken to Daniel and me was igniting something deep inside me.

The Head looked at me following my outburst. He straightened his back and coughed.

'Mr Williamson, as a school we pride ourselves on the pastoral care we provide for all our children. But we are a school and our primary role is the education of our children. While I sympathise with the problems at home it is not within my capacity to support every child with their home life.'

'But surely if home life is having an impact on school life then you do have a duty?' I asked thinking that this wasn't rocket science and if I could see it surely other people could too.

The Head did not respond to me, instead he looked at Daniel.

'Daniel, let's go and see if we can placate Miss Smith.'

And with that he and Daniel set off down the long corridor.

'Bye Daniel' I said as I watched them disappear into a classroom.

My heart felt for Daniel; although he had avoided any sanctions I think the tone from the Head was sufficient to let him know that he had clearly been in the wrong and that he needed to re-think his behaviour.

I left the school feeling angry and hurt; for a fleeting moment I was taken back to the fifteen year old me who spent more time leaving school than actually attending. I was transported back to my old school and the lane that ran parallel to the Victorian buildings that held so many narratives for generations of children. If only I could turn back the clock I thought as I climbed into the car.

As I drove home I replayed the conversation with the Head. I started to think about what I could do about the situation at school. I was convinced that the Head was wrong. Surely schools had a moral duty to take into consideration factors that might be affecting their pupils. Yes, I knew their primary role was to educate but how the hell could children learn when their minds were preoccupied with worries? How the hell was Daniel expected to carry on being the model pupil when he was so worried about his Mum and all that was happening at home? I felt frustrated, maybe I should have said more to the Head, maybe I should have stood my ground and argued more for Daniel. Maybe I should have been more of a man and stood up for my son. I wondered, as I neared home, what would my old man have done in that situation?

SEVENTEEN

Angela

Sleep was one of the things I struggled with because of IT. I found it difficult to get comfortable in bed and was conscious of tossing and turning. It seemed that as soon as I got to bed my mind started to play cruel tricks on me. People always said that problems seemed worse in the middle of the night and that was so true for me. I could lie awake watching the minutes clicking away on our bedside clock, my mind racing with all sorts of worries. And when I did go to sleep I kept having disturbing dreams. These generally involved Nathan and the children and were always dark and frightening. In them I was usually running away from them and I could hear their cries for me to come back but I would take no heed and keep running until my lungs felt that they were going to burst. It was generally at that point that I woke up sweating. I would try hard not to disturb Nathan but he would wake too. Initially he was really worried about the dreams but with time learnt to just hold me close and reassure me about where I was and that I was safe.

One night I had a particularly disturbing dream. At the point of my lungs exploding I didn't wake up, instead I carried on running until I entered a building through a heavy revolving door which I struggled to open. It was maybe an office, I was unsure but there were hundreds of faces watching my every action. In the dream I tried to escape, to run back out of the building I had foolishly entered but I couldn't. All the doors had disappeared, there were no windows. I was a prisoner. Still the faces stared at me through the yellow light from the strip-lighting that illuminated the room. Each pair of eyes critically appraising me. I tried to scream but no noise would escape from my mouth; I was silenced and trapped. On one wall a massive clock hung at an angle.

As the dream continued to unravel, its cruel plot entrapping me, I was being visited by a social worker. He was really tall and had broad shoulders. He wore a black suit, shirt and tie and looked officious and intimidating. He was shouting at me that I was a bad mother and that I wasn't fit to look after my children. He kept pointing his index finger at me and then started pushing it into my shoulder. I could feel his breath on my face and smell his over-powering aftershave. He said he was going to take the children away from me and find someone decent who had the capability to be a good, caring mother. He kept repeating that I was a poor mother and shouldn't be allowed to have children. His voice getting louder and louder each time he spoke those cruel words.

Thankfully at that point I was released from the dream and woke up sobbing. Nathan held me in his arms until I was able to incoherently tell him about the dream. Through my sobs I told him how frightened I was that Social Services would remove the children. I knew that I was not being the same mother to them. I was no longer able to take Titch to all her after-school groups and simply didn't have the energy to provide the same level of care that I had done previously. I was clearly no longer doing an adequate job with Daniel or he wouldn't have had that very close scrape with the police and school. What if the dream was an omen, a message warning me that I would lose the children because of becoming an inadequate mum?

Nathan tried to reassure me, but no words were sufficient to convince me that I had not failed my children.

In my angst I could not see anything but failure.

It was a long night for both of us.

* * *

The next day I felt I was in a very dark place. Physically I was coping quite well with the treatment but emotionally I was really struggling. I was energy-less and hadn't bothered to get washed and dressed after Nathan had taken Titch to school. I sat on the settee with the television on. I wasn't really watching what was on but the constant noise was reassuring and helped dull the noise in my head which kept telling me that I was a bad mother.

Initially I didn't hear the knock on the door, it was only when it became louder and more frantic that I realised there was somebody there. I froze.

The urgency of the banging must be the sound a social worker makes when they are trying to remove children from their homes. I knew the man in the nightmare had come to take Titch and Daniel away. Even in my confused state I knew that I must not let him in, I knew I must keep away from the window and pretend I was not there. How would Titch cope going to live with a stranger? Would they separate Titch and Daniel or have the good grace to find a foster home where they could both go? How would Daniel cope? He had been struggling lately and had been quite difficult to manage. *'Oh shit'* I thought as I tried to stay quiet. His behaviour had been the tipping point, the trouble at school and the brief issues with those boys and the car. Because I couldn't parent him properly they had come to take him and Titch away from me.

The knocking continued and then my mobile telephone started ringing. I managed to reach for it, being careful to get it without being noticed through the window. I looked and saw it was Elspeth's number. I answered it being as quiet as I could.

'Angela,' a very worried voice 'Angela are you okay, let me in I've been hammering on the door for ages, are you okay?' I could hear the rising panic in Elspeth's voice.

'Where are you?'

'Outside your door, are you going to let me in or shall I break the bloody thing down?' she said half laughing, but I could hear the concern in her voice.

'Sorry, I must have been asleep, hang on I'll come and unlock it.'

I felt dazed and confused, was it really Elspeth at the door or was she a decoy being used by the social worker. Was he using her to gain access to the house?

I looked through the partial glass in the door and could make out the shape of a woman's body. I tentatively unlocked the door and opened it just sufficiently to see Elspeth's distinctive red and yellow rain mac.

Elspeth kissed my cheek as she walked in, 'some sleep' was her only comment.

I looked into the road, there were no signs of any strange cars or people, all was quiet. I quickly closed the door behind us and locked it. Elspeth noticed and looked puzzled 'oh it's rough round here' I said trying to make a joke of my actions. Elspeth didn't say anything.

Elspeth led the way into our sitting room and sat on the usual settee. It crossed my mind how we were all creatures of habit; is it somehow us trying to maintain the routines that clearly define who we are and our actions? The normality of her actions helped bring me back to the here and now. This wasn't a sinister visit; it was a good friend who had called round to see me, although I was unsure of her motives. She must have read my mind, 'Nathan rang this morning, said you might need a bit of company, just thought I'd pop in on my way to the shops.'

The ritual of routines kicked in again when I realised I should be offering my visitor a coffee. Elspeth accepted and followed me into the kitchen. She leaned against the doorjamb as I put the kettle on.

'So how much did Nathan tell you?' I asked.

'He just said that you'd had a particularly rough night and that it had left you feeling a bit fragile.'

'Yeah, something like that, sounds about right' I observed.

We remained in silence while I continued to make the drinks. I had my back to Elspeth but I could sense that she was watching me and my every move. Once the kettle had boiled and I had made the drinks we went back into the sitting room. Elspeth spoke briefly about the weather and how food prices seemed to be going up every time she went to the supermarket.

After a sip of her steaming coffee, Elspeth asked if I wanted to talk about my dream. I did, I really did but I wasn't sure where to begin and what sense it would make to anyone who had not been there. I told her as much and with her usual gentle persuasive nature she suggested I might like to try and that she would decide if I was making any sense.

I gave her a potted version, starting with the fact that since the diagnosis I regularly had bad dreams that had a recurring theme running through them. I went on to tell her how the one the previous night had seemed to be an accumulation of all the others. It combined all the nasty bits into one massively scary and real nightmare.

As I recalled the dream again the same panic began to rise from the pit of my stomach.

I could feel the fear wrapping itself around me and squeezing the little bit of energy I had out from my body and mind. I stopped talking and took time to drink my coffee. Elspeth remained quiet, listening intently to my story and, I suspect, trying to think about the most appropriate way to respond.

Recalling the dream opened the floodgates. The memories of it putting into stark focus the fears that I had been harbouring for some time. Without giving Elspeth time to respond about the dream I started talking about the worries and concerns I had about the children and the reality that I might be seen as being a bad mother and that they might be taken away from me. As I spoke I realised that the dream had been a manifestation of all the worries that I had been trying to keep at bay. I suppose during the day I had, to some extent, a bit of control over my thoughts. When I was feeling vulnerable and scared about the future I could try hard to distract myself or to constructively manage what I was thinking about. But at night it was a different thing altogether. At night in the dark I was alone with the worries and fears. The quiet clicking of the bedside clock measuring the passing of each minute, each hour, each moment in my life. During the night I had less control and it was then that my dark subconscious mind started playing out its evil predictions.

As I spoke about my genuine concern that the children would be removed tears started to roll down my cheek. My head was pounding as I heard my voice betraying me. Until now I had not shared those fears, preferring to keep them to myself. If they were made public, people would see more of my vulnerability and at that point there was enough of that without adding into the mix the fear of losing the children because of being an inadequate mother.

Elspeth reached into her handbag and passed me a tissue. I dabbed my eyes hoping that the action would stem the flow of tears but it didn't. She moved to sit next to me on the settee. She gently held my hand but remained silent. I looked into her eyes, searching for an answer, searching for reassurance that I wasn't a bad mother and that the children would not be taken into care because of all my inadequacies. Her eyes gave little away other than concern; they too had tears in them but Elspeth managed to control them.

I'm not sure how long we sat for in the quiet. Time became irrelevant as I tried in my mind to process all that I had shared with Elspeth. After what seemed like an age, I finally managed to stem the flow of tears. My eyes felt heavy and achy and I guessed my face would be a red mess.

Elspeth picked up our coffee cups 'let's have a fresh one?' she asked as she made her way into the kitchen. I went to the bathroom and rinsed my face with cold water. I briefly looked in the mirror and noticed I was right, one big blotchy red mess. As IT had taken hold I had tried to avoid looking in the mirror. I didn't like what I saw looking back at me and so found it easier to ignore it. I used to take such pride in my looks; my hair and make-up were an important presentation of who I was and therefore I felt it important to take time to care to ensure that they were right. Because of IT I had neither the energy nor the inclination. IT had ensured that any traces of femininity had temporarily left me. The treatment had affected the condition of my hair and skin and I had lost the healthy glow which was one of my treasured features. Initially I worried about this greatly but became resigned to the fact that my body was a representation of IT and although I disliked it immensely I had sort of come to terms with it. I had reconciled the fact that this was part of the journey with IT and that there were far more serious consequences that I was struggling to come to terms with.

Back in the sitting room there were two fresh cups of steaming coffee. Elspeth was sitting back in her usual spot and to an outsider looking in everything would have appeared normal and controlled.

'Sorry' was the only thing I could think to say to Elspeth, 'bit of a bad day.'

Elspeth looked at me over the rim of her cup and took a deep breath 'it sounds as though you've been holding on to that for far too long.'

I made no comment but feebly nodded my head. I had been holding it all for too long she was quite right but how do you begin to share such fears even if you really want to. *'Oh hi, thanks for calling round, by the way I think I'm being a really bad mother and suspect Social Services will come and take my children away.'* It wasn't that easy and if it hadn't been for the nightmare the previous night and Nathan's telephone call to Elspeth it would still have been locked deep in my heart and head.

'You know, I think I can understand what you are saying' said Elspeth in a soft voice. 'It sounds as though you've had a really difficult time with the dreams and all those thoughts and because of that there have been some cruel tricks played. Sometimes when we are in a dark place our minds can be really awful. But I also think that maybe some of your worries are unfounded. Why do you think Social Services will take the children away from you? What's making you think that?'

'I, err, well because of all that has happened since Christmas. IT has taken over my life and my family's life, it is all we ever seem to talk about and think about. The children can't do what they used to do; sometimes I just don't have the energy to cook the evening meal. Look at me I'm a wreck. Daniel has really struggled with it all and I suppose he still is, and Titch is a different child, her light has gone out.' My voice caught and I thought I was going to start crying again but thankfully I was able to stop the tears.

'Let's look at this' said Elspeth. I could tell she was choosing her words with great care.

'Yes it is all very rubbish, there is no denying that and yes things have changed because of IT. But you are still doing a grand job with the children. Of course they have blips, come on they are worried sick about you, but they are coping in their own way. And what about you? You are still there for them; you are still loving them and being the same mother, in a slightly different way. And you've got good support from family and friends. I can understand that you are very worried about the children and about your role as their mum but nobody is going to take them off you. Social Services aren't going to get involved with your family; you really aren't bad enough for that just yet.'

I glanced up at her and saw a wry smile on her face. 'Seriously', she said, now in full counselling flow 'you are still providing them with love, warmth and shelter, what more do they need?'

'What more do they need' I thought to myself, well maybe a mother that was going to stick around long enough to see them grow up for a start. I might miss Rebecca's graduation and not be there for Daniel and his GSCEs. I might not see Titch in her new school uniform when she

moves to the comprehensive school. I might not be there for their weddings, or babies or anything.

This time I could not stop the flow of tears. Tears of sadness and pity. Tears of anger and frustration. Tears for a lost future.

EIGHTEEN

Rebecca

As Mum's illness took its seemingly inevitable course, I found myself talking more and more to Dora. She was a good listener and rarely tried to tell me how I should be feeling or what I should be feeling. Instead she gave me the space I needed to explore all that was happening and try to begin to understand the implications of IT.

If I was feeling particularly depressed or frustrated by what was happening I would text her and ask if it was convenient to call and see her. I tried very hard not to talk to her when we were at work. I didn't want her to get into trouble with Dave and also the museum café was just not a conducive environment to start talking about personal, painful things.

Dora lived in a terraced house on a neat and tidy street quite close to the centre of the city. The houses appeared to be cared for and there was a sense of pride in the street. All the houses had a small garden leading to the front door. Dora had planted lavender into the ground and had a variety of pots by the door which had annual plants in. The pots offered some colour and made the entrance to the house very cheery and welcoming. The front door led straight into the living room. When I first visited Dora, I could tell that she had a natural flair for interior designs. The room was cosy and full of bright colours which complimented each other. There was a big pitcher filled with flowers and colourful candles dotted about the room. I guessed from the knitted cushions that either Dora or somebody in her family was a keen knitter. I passed comment about the room and how much I liked the style. Dora became quite coy and thanked me for the compliment before admitting that she had studied fine art at college. She said that one day she would like to explore her options for having that as a career but for now was content looking after her boys.

I always felt calm when I went to see Dora. No matter how much my emotions had churned up inside me they were lessened when I sat in her comfy little room. When I went to see her she would generally ask quite broad questions about how Mum was and how I was feeling. This gave me the space to then start talking about my worries. I felt safe with Dora, I felt confident that she was not going to judge me because of what I said to her. I felt confident that she was not going to undermine my feelings or speak in platitudes that were meaningless. I think most of all I felt confident that I would be listened to and that there would be some shared understanding of what I was going through. I knew that Dora was not going to tell me what I should be doing, or what I should be feeling. Instead she was going to listen and help me to help myself work through my emotions and feelings. I knew that Dora did not have the answers, I knew that nobody had the answers, but I was also aware that as I tried to articulate what I was feeling, Dora's presence was helping me to think through possible solutions. I knew that my talking about IT was not going to help make Mum better and it was not going to make IT go away, but maybe, just maybe it would help me to think through the pain. Maybe that was the best I could hope for right now.

During one of my visits to see Dora, she mentioned in passing, that after her Mum had died she wrote down all her feelings in a notebook. She said that she scribbled furiously as she tried to write down all her emotions, anger and sadness at the death. She said it was difficult because her thoughts spewed out with such speed and force her writing couldn't keep up. She remembered how after the initial writing she would return to the notebook to add in new thoughts as they came to her. I asked Dora whether that had been helpful to her. She thought carefully before she replied. I guessed she was thinking back, possibly replaying those days and trying to capture what had been the outcome of her writings. She acknowledged that it had been a very difficult thing to do but that she was also glad that she had done it as it had given her the opportunity to express herself through the safety of the written word. The notebook was private and did not need to be shared with anyone, and I suspect it gave Dora a sense of safety and control. The contents could remain between Dora and the pages of the notebook; it could be a personal link to her dead mother that would give her some connection.

As I walked back to my room, I thought about Dora's conversation about her notebook and how it had, in some small way, helped her to find a way to navigate the pain she was feeling because of her Mum's death. The thought struck me that maybe I should do something similar now. I wondered whether by writing a letter to IT I too might find some better understanding of my feelings.

Back in my room I immediately found some note paper and my favourite green pen that Mum had bought me once when we were staying at Granny's. I wrote my first and last letter to IT.

Dear IT,

I suppose you don't really know me, you clearly don't care about me or you wouldn't be controlling my family with your cruel, malicious actions. I wish I knew why you chose my family. We are just an ordinary family trying to get on with our lives. Mum and Dad work hard and have always been good parents to me and my brother and sister. They wouldn't hurt anyone and, as far as I can remember, have never said a bad thing about anyone. What gave you the right to come into our family and make us all so unhappy? What exactly do you want to achieve by doing this? Do you know how sad and frightened you are making us all feel? Do you care? I don't suppose you do or you wouldn't be here. Do you have to be so invasive? Now that you have spread your nastiness can't you leave us alone and let us get on with our lives? If you went now, Mum would have a chance to get better and we could just pick up where we were before you took it upon yourself to be the uninvited guest in our house. You are making me feel so very frightened, I'm scared that soon I won't have a mum and it will be all your fault. What will I do if she dies? How will I get over that, how will any of us get over it? I hate you and all that you stand for. Please, please, please go away and leave us alone.

I couldn't bring myself to sign the letter, and what did it matter if I didn't. I read and re-read it, bitter tears of resentment running down my face. It was less than 300 words long but I felt exhausted when I had finished writing it. That short note held so much of what I was feeling, of what I wanted to say, of what I needed to express. But who was there to say those things to? I could be angry with God or the doctors or the person down the street; but in reality who could I be angry with?

Writing the letter had helped me to focus my feelings and briefly to explore how IT was affecting me. From my writing I could see the unfairness of it all and the pain that the illness had brought not just to Mum but to all of us, individually and collectively. I think Dora was right when she said that getting feelings out in the open could be beneficial.

It didn't stop IT and it certainly didn't make IT go away but it did help me to think about what IT represented. I realised that IT was far more than just something that was making Mum sick. IT was far more divisive than that, invading every aspect of our lives and turning all our granted ways upside down. The illness represented change, change that was going to impact on our family not just today and next week but for ever. I knew that my family would never be the same again. The diagnosis had ensured that we would all have to adjust to a different life.

I deliberately left the letter out on the small multi-functional table in my room. Whenever I sat at the table to either work or eat I saw it and emotionally connected with it. Every time I saw it I was reminded of the pain it contained and the unfairness of it all. I vehemently hoped that IT would know that I had penned a letter to express how evil it was.

NINETEEN

Nathan

'Come on, join in' I said as I burst in to song 'we're all going away to see Granny, no more school for a day or two.'

Titch and Daniel giggled. The prospect of a few days away had sparked much excitement and anticipation. The fact that it was a very last minute decision just added to their growing delight.

We had had a few weeks where IT had been more controlled and as a result Angela's health had been quite stable. As Mr Gough had noted at our last appointment we had reached a good plateau. His prophetic words of advice being that we should enjoy this period. And so with uncharacteristic spontaneity we had telephoned Angela's Mum to see whether she could cope with a mini visit from us. I was aware it was a bit of an imposition asking her; she'd only been home a few weeks following a brief stay with us to help out. But with our finances being as they were it would have been difficult to manage going anywhere other than Norfolk. Also I knew that Angela felt safe at her Mum's and if there was another medical emergency we could quickly get help. Angela's Mum had agreed to our stay before we had finished asking her. And so there we were heading back down the A17 towards our second home.

I thought back to the last time I had driven that stretch of road. It had been for our Christmas break and I had been blissfully unaware of the traumas that the New Year would bring. I thought how quickly things can change and how you are never prepared for such catastrophic life events. In the blink of an eye my life had been turned upside down and I felt it would never right itself again. This was the new norm for us, a difficult, painful chapter in our family's life. One of the hardest things was not knowing how the chapter would end. I had written and re-written the plot that I wanted to happen. Of course I had. It involved a happy ending and a miracle of medicine; it was all about Angela getting better and us slowly putting the last few months behind us as we re-built our family. It had included tears of joy and relief and adjustment and coping. But most of all it had involved healing and moving forward. But in reality in the dark place where I currently was I knew that my version of the future was a thing of fantasy. I was beginning to know in my heart of hearts that this chapter was not going to have the fairy tale ending we all so craved.

I pushed all such thoughts away and tried to bury them deep in the back of my mind. Angela was looking better than she had for ages, the sun was shining and we were going away for a few days; let's enjoy and make the most of what we have now.

The children's excitement at missing school and the prospect of time on the beach was palpable. It was mid-June, Rebecca was home for the summer holidays having successfully completed her first year at university and our estate car's boot was groaning under the weight of all the stuff we had packed.

Because we were travelling out of season the roads were pleasantly quiet, just the usual hold ups with tractors and a few HGVs. 'First one to see the sea wins the prize' I shouted into the back of the car. The children groaned in unison, knowing full well that we were not taking the coast road down to the cottage and so would not be seeing the sea until we had arrived at Gran's house. I grinned and looked at Angela. She glanced across and smiled a wry smile 'torment' was her only comment.

We arrived at Angela's Mum's cottage in time for a late lunch. As always the children quickly made the neat and tidy living room look as though a typhoon had blown through as they unceremoniously dumped their holiday gear on the floor. The smell of freshly baked bread and asparagus quiche wafted in from the kitchen.

Angela's Mum was beaming at the arrival of her family and the nod to normality. After hugs and kisses she was off making tea and sorting out the salad.

'I thought we'd have it in the garden if that's okay' she called from the kitchen.

Lunch was delicious and most welcome following the long drive. Afterwards we sat in the pretty cottage garden chatting and catching up with the gossip from the village. I was unsure whether it was Angela or her mother who was trying valiantly to create a sense of normalcy but the un-health related conversations, the warm sun and the sound of blackbirds singing generated a peaceful antidote to the previous few months. I relaxed back in my deckchair and sighed a long sigh of relief. Just for now we were going to carry on as normal; we were going to make some solid memories of happy times. I was determined that I was going to make sure that any thoughts of IT were going to be locked away as deeply as possible in my mind.

'*I'm the man of the house*', I thought to myself and while we are here and safe I am going to try my hardest to protect my family from the realities of this cruel blow. For a few days we can be ourselves. And with that I closed my eyes and drifted off into a pleasant afternoon nap.

The weather the following day personified June. There was a cloudless blue sky and by 9.00 am when Angela and I woke it was already bee-buzzing warm. The smell of the climbing rose and honeysuckle wafted into our bedroom. We had both slept well, our sleep blissfully un-peppered by disturbing dreams. Often Angela struggled in the mornings. Her tiredness preventing her from being as active as she would like, however, that morning was different. She was pain free and was refreshed from a good night's sleep.

The children were already up, dressed and eating breakfast when Angela and I went into the kitchen. Angela's mum greeted us with a choice for breakfast 'will it be a cooked breakfast Sir?' she asked me 'and you Madam?' We both opted for cereal and toast; the memories of the home baked bread at lunch yesterday still fresh in my mind. I was not disappointed; the butter melted into the soft bread and the homemade Seville orange marmalade was the perfect partner. I ate slowly, appreciating the taste of every mouthful. I imagined the lads at work watching me eat with such refined pleasure, how they would laugh if they could see me now I thought. I could almost hear their playful ridicule '*get a bacon butty and a mug of tea down you.*' With that I took a sip of the Earl Grey tea that Angela's Mum had poured from her china teapot into the delicate china cups she always got out for high days and holidays. I smiled to myself as I tried in vain to hook my little finger round the handle of the cup.

After breakfast we set off for a morning on the beach. Angela's Mum declined the offer of a trip, preferring instead to stay and prepare lunch. I suspect that was her selfless way of giving us some time as a family. However, before we left she did hand over a wicker basket filled with flasks of tea and coffee, orange squash and freshly made buttered scones. She smiled at me as she passed it over 'just in case you get peckish' she said with a twinkle in her eye. Once again I marvelled at her energy. She must have been up early to bake the scones and prepare everything. Yet another wave of gratitude swept over me.

We had a lovely few hours on the beach. The children insisted on having a paddle, and although the prospect was tempting, I decided not to join them. Much as the sand was pleasantly warm the sea still looked cold and I decided that my ageing legs would not cope with the shock. Daniel was not as eager as Titch and Rebecca but he did play the dutiful brother role and had a quick dip before the smell of coffee enticed him back to us.

Angela and I sat on the beach in silence enjoying the moment. I watched the children playing, their gleeful squeals intermittently breaking the otherwise quiet surroundings. The only other sound was the sea gently lapping onto the beach. As the tide ebbed over the pebbles and pulled them back towards the sea it made a percussive sound that was calming and almost hypnotic.

There were very few people about. A few couples walked along the shoreline but for the most part we had the beach to ourselves.

After their mandatory paddle the girls came back to join us. Titch made a few sandcastles with architectural and construction advice from Daniel. Angela watched them playing then nudged my arm with her elbow, and questioned in a whisper 'taking after his Dad?' We both smiled. It was good to watch them playing together and actually getting on. When Daniel was struggling to come to terms with the news of IT he had not been the nicest person to be around and had been particularly mean to Titch. There had been countless arguments and disagreements between them mainly over very minor issues. Initially I had been angry with Daniel and because of that the arguments had escalated. It was only after the incident with Miss Smith, the youths and the police that I started to try and better understand his behaviour. My blinkers had finally been partially lifted and I was, for the first time, really seeing how IT was impacting on the children.

When I had spoken to Daniel and had time to think about all that was happening and how it was affecting him I started to understand just a little more about what was making him behave as he was. I started to realise that IT was the cause of his behaviour and that it was his way of releasing some of the anger and pain that had been tormenting him. Part of this had been that he had interpreted our overt protection of Titch as being a sign of us caring for her more than him and therefore, in his eyes, he was being rejected by us. That had been a brief but incredibly difficult period to manage and reflecting back I think I should have handled it very differently. But how could I have handled it differently? Nobody was there telling me what to do, nobody was helping Angela and me to continue parenting through the crap that IT had brought into our family. Nobody seemed to care how we were coping. So why should I have known?

As we sat amidst the safety of a family day on the beach I could hear the voice of reason in the form of Ryan '*Come on mate, how the hell do you expect to know what is best for the kids? How are you supposed to know how best to parent them under such circumstances? This isn't your average family crisis you are trying to manage, for God's sake your wife is ill, and nobody ever prepares you for that.'*

In my heart I knew that Ryan was right, of course he was. When your partner is pregnant you get the opportunity to go to antenatal classes and are given advice about becoming a parent. When your partner is diagnosed with an illness that is potentially life-limiting the same support does not apply. Oh no this time you are on your own so get on with it. But that isn't easy. We were fortunate to have a good informal support network, we had a good relationship as a family – 'Team Williamson rules' and Angela and I were both quite savvy parents and yet we struggled. How did families cope when there wasn't the same extent of support or modicum of parenting skills that we had? I felt for them, I really did.

My thoughts were brought back to the present when I heard Rebecca asking about Granny's scones and suggesting that it might be time to try them. *'That's my girl'* I thought proudly as I looked over to where she was sitting on the beach. Angela carefully poured more coffee then delved back into the wicker basket to find the tin with the scones in along with a small jar of freshly made strawberry jam. As I would have expected they were delicious and we all ate quietly enjoying, with pleasure, Granny's baking.

Before heading back to the cottage for lunch we had a short walk along the beach. Titch and Daniel ran ahead playing tag and Rebecca walked some paces behind us lost for a while in her own contemplations.

Once or twice as we were walking, I saw Titch look my way, a concerned expression on her face. I wondered whether she was remembering her recurring nightmare where I sailed away on different boats and left the family helplessly watching me go.

After lunch, Angela went to bed for a rest. She said that the fresh air and good food had made her sleepy. I hoped it was just that and that the holiday wasn't too much for her now beleaguered body to cope with. The drugs that Mr Gough and his team had prescribed were helping control IT but the side effects were making their own problems. Tiredness was the primary issue to affect her. This was difficult for Angela to accept as, prior to IT she had always been on the go and always full of energy and life. On more than one occasion she had broken down in tears at the unfairness of being so lethargic. She hated not being able to do the same things with the children as she had done previously and that she had had to reluctantly give up her gym subscription 'just until I am better'. The children and I had tried to adjust accordingly to support Angela. Our pace of family life in turn slowing down to match her energy levels. That was a difficult adjustment to make as slow motion was not the traditional Williamson way.

That created frustrations for the children, especially Titch who became increasingly angry with me and Angela because she couldn't do the same things as before. We had had to curtail some of her after school activities; the shear logistics of managing them became too difficult. Without the support of friends it was impossible to keep up transporting her to and from her different clubs and activities. In addition, although I never admitted this to her, our financial state also meant that we were finding it difficult to afford to pay for all the groups. That was especially the situation when I had reduced my hours to the minimum and the bank had started chasing me for the mortgage. I'd always taken pride in the fact that through my hard work we had enough money to pay the bills and to have a reasonably comfortable time. But when I had to choose between work and caring for Angela things began to get difficult. Another bit of my identity was stripped away from me. Not only had I been robbed of my role as man of the house I was also no longer the provider that I wanted and needed to be. Once again I was letting my family down and was failing in my role.

After our evening meal, the children and I went for a walk into the woods. All three of them were happy to accept my invitation for them to join me. Angela and her Mum opted to stay at home and spend some time together. It was a perfectly still evening with no breeze and not a cloud in the sky. Titch and Rebecca went on ahead, Titch tightly holding on to Rebecca's hand. Daniel and I followed a little behind. For the most part we walked in silence but this time it was a comfortable silence, not like the awful time when we had walked round the lake near home. Occasionally we would stop and listen as an animal had been disturbed by our presence. We stood quietly trying to see if we could see what it was and were rewarded with a glimpse of a buck muntjac. The sunlight caught his copper brown fur as he spotted us and bounded away into the wood. Above us in the tree canopy there was the constant sound of bird song. I listened carefully, allowing the sweet sound to be absorbed by my every fibre. The peace and tranquillity was almost overpowering. It was the antithesis of all that had been happening in my world for the last six months. For a few minutes I stood in silence lost in a happy, calm place. I thought about how nature would be playing out its life-cycle all over the country and how life was going on even though for me it felt as though it was standing still. For the first time in ages I felt a peace that I had not enjoyed for a long time. The worries about not being able to provide for my family, or not being a good enough husband or father were soothed away with the stillness of the woods.

It was beginning to get dark when we got back to the cottage. Titch was getting weary after a busy day and so after a mug of hot milk happily went to bed. Rebecca, Angela and Angela's Mum soon followed. Daniel and I sat out in the garden enjoying the last of the day's warmth. It was now dark and the sky had transformed into a magical celestial picture show. At home there was so much light pollution we rarely got chance to see more than a handful of stars so neither Daniel nor I wanted to miss the stargazing opportunity. We tried to identify the different constellations and stars. I had a little knowledge gleaned from time spent with an uncle when I was a boy. He used to know all the major constellations and would share stories about each one. I remember being fascinated by his tales. But then after Dad died I lost interest. Following his funeral a well-meaning neighbour told me that Dad was now a star in the sky and that he would be looking down on me. Initially I got great comfort from that but then one cloudy night I looked out of my bedroom window to see him and there was nothing. I couldn't see any stars, let alone my Dad's. I was gutted and mourned the second loss of my father.

Daniel and I stopped out for quite a while just marvelling at the stars and the prospect of what was out there beyond our little world. Again we were mainly in silence but again I was content with that. It was Daniel who broke the silence.

'Dad' he asked tentatively 'do you think there is a heaven up there?'

I glanced at him trying to work out how he wanted me to answer that.

'No Daniel, I'm not sure whether there is up there, but what I do believe is that there is somewhere people go after they have died. I really don't know where it is or what happens, but I do think there is somewhere.'

I wasn't sure whether my answer had been sufficient to satisfy his question.

'What do you think Daniel, do think there might be?'

'It's a big space up there; surely dead people have to go somewhere.'

'I think the thing to remember Dan is that the dead never leave our hearts as long as we have space for them.'

Daniel looked at me and smiled. 'I know that' was his only reply.

We sat for a while longer looking at the night sky and thinking our own private thoughts. A gentle breeze got up and the warmth of the day started to fade.

'Come on, time for bed I think. We've got another busy day tomorrow exploring and eating Granny out of house and home.'

As we went into the house I gently touched Daniel's arm 'good night Dan, try and get some sleep.'

'Night Dad, thank you.'

TWENTY

Nathan

My mobile telephone rang; I could see from the screen that it was Ryan.

'Hello Nathan, how are you doing mate? I've not seen you for ages do you fancy a pint next Thursday?'

Following my pathetic exhibition at the rugby club where I had bared my soul to Ryan and most of the other supporters, we'd not had much contact. Immediately after that night he had telephoned a couple of times to see how I was but then things got in the way. Ryan was busy with his family trying to sort out buying a caravan. His wife had got this idea that it would be really good to have a static caravan at the coast where they could go every weekend in the summer. From the bit he had told me it sounded as though she had made her mind up and so it was all systems go to find one. I'd been busy juggling work and looking after Angela and so we just hadn't met up and had only exchanged a few telephone calls. In part I had also wanted to avoid seeing him again. I felt so ashamed of my behaviour and was furious with myself for showing, in public, my weaknesses.

'Ryan, how are you? Have you got your new home by the sea yet?'

I knew that Ryan wasn't particularly bothered about the caravan but when his Tish got an idea it generally meant that whatever her plan was it would come to fruition.

Ryan groaned 'oh mate just don't go there, will tell you all when I see you. How do you fancy a pint?'

'Let me check with Ange but it should be okay, it would be nice to catch up. I'll ring nearer the time to confirm if that is okay.'

'Looking forward to it Mate, take care, bye.'

Actually I was quite looking forward to meeting up with Ryan. We'd not been out for ages and the thought of going out with my friend for a few pints seemed very appealing. When I mentioned it to Angela she immediately said that I should go and that it would do me good. I sent Ryan a text and arranged to meet him. I also promised I wouldn't bring the Drama Queen with me. His text was short and to the point – LOL.

It felt very strange retracing my steps back to the rugby club. I'd not walked that route since that awful night in April. I had decided to leave the car at home being aware that just two pints would be far more than I had drunk for ages and would be likely to affect my driving. As I walked towards the club I thought back about the last few months.

I suppose not much had changed really; in some respects things had got a lot worse but on the whole things were pretty much as they had been when I last saw Ryan. Angela and I were still trying to come to terms with the news and adjusting to a new life with IT as the third person in our relationship. It felt as though whatever we wanted to do, whatever we planned needed to include IT. If we wanted to go out for the day we needed to consider whether Angela had any appointments or what treatments she was due. We needed to see how she was feeling and whether she had had a bad night and so therefore was too tired to do what we had planned. There was always the checking process – how was she feeling physically and mentally, was it a good day or a bad day? All those silly little things that we had never considered before had suddenly become part of our daily lives. All conversations seemed to lead down just one road. It felt as though every time I spoke to someone their first question was *'how is Angela'* followed by questions about IT and the treatment and what the doctors had said. I knew this was just people being really concerned and caring about her but it was so draining. I didn't even talk about the weather anymore in idle conversations unless it was related to how the cold, warmth, rain or wind was affecting IT and making Angela feel. The days of just talking about work and rugby and bloke things had gone. There was only one topic of conversation.

And in the midst of all this we were trying desperately hard to keep things as normal as possible for our all our sakes but especially the children's. Angela and I had made an unspoken decision to carry on as normally as possible. We didn't want to unduly alarm the children and we didn't want them to feel as though normal life had stopped and everything was revolving round IT. But despite our best efforts to shield them IT was still managing to get in the way.

When Daniel had got into trouble at school I went through waves of anger. At first I was furious with him. How stupid and irresponsible could he be getting into a car with two boys he didn't know and driving off with them. Anything could have happened to him that day, most of which were not worth thinking about. He was lucky that the police had not got involved and for that I was very grateful. But what if the lad had lost control when he was driving? Daniel could have been another statistic being cut out from the wrangled mess of the car. For a while after, the image of the fire brigade using their specialist cutters to cut him out from the car haunted me. I could see in minute detail them frantically working to save our boy's life. I could hear them shouting to each other "*Steve, there's another kid in the back we need to get the roof off, quick he's not responding*". And then I had the image of a police officer standing at our door "*Mr Williamson, can I come in Sir I've got some bad news*". Then there was the inevitable inquest where Angela and I had to give evidence to the Coroner and then the headlines in the local weekly rag. In my imagination our sad story even made the local news on television. They used an old photograph of Daniel and then cut across to a picture of the wrecked car. The head teacher was interviewed saying what a wonderful pupil Daniel had been, especially in relation to his sporting achievements and that he would be sadly missed by the school community.

After the initial anger at Daniel I then moved my annoyance to school. So many memories came back about the times I, and then Ryan and I, had bunked off from school for no particular reason other than it was not meeting our needs. But in those days it all seemed very different and all we did was sit by the canal trying to bomb floating debris with any stones or missiles that we could lay our hands on. Daniel's situation felt very different. School had been aware of things at home; they knew about Angela's illness and the stress that we were all under. Why hadn't Miss Smith shown an ounce of compassion and not been so heavy on the lad. I did, when I had calmed down, acknowledge that maybe it was the systems fault and not especially Miss Smith's. If they had a procedure to follow to ensure that appropriate support was in place at times of a crisis then that might not have arisen. It seemed to my simplistic mind that schools had procedures for just about every eventuality but not about this.

But with or without things in place I was still furious with them. Their behaviour had set off a chain of events that could have ended so differently. Daniel had felt compelled to leave his class; he'd then met up with two dubious characters and ended up driving round the country in a stolen car. Great pastoral care I thought. But inevitably my anger then moved back to IT. If it wasn't for IT then Angela wouldn't have been rushed into hospital, Daniel wouldn't have been worried sick and would have been more interested in Miss Smith and the rock formations within the Grand Canyon and then he wouldn't have ended up in the bus station café. So once again the anger and frustration stopped squarely with IT.

Titch was harder to read. At least when Daniel had his blip we were acutely aware of it and could therefore do something about it, but with Titch it was different. She had been quieter and not really said much although sometimes her behaviour had been different. It was almost as if someone had flicked a light switch and she changed. During those spells she'd been much more irritable with all of us. That had been difficult for us to manage, especially Angela who had tried to carry on parenting as normal but who had struggled when our placid little girl had started being tetchy and occasionally very angry. Although this had happened at home it had been more apparent in school and there had been a number of occasions where Mrs Rigsby had telephoned to tell Angela that Titch's behaviour had landed her in trouble. When we tried to talk to Titch about this she just shrugged her shoulders and found it hard to give any explanations for her behaviour. Thankfully, once Angela had met with the head teacher and had told them about IT they had been better able to manage Titch's behaviour.

I think it had been especially difficult for Rebecca. Being away from home made her feel isolated and that had not helped her at all. We noticed a pattern with her; when she came home she always said that she wanted to stay and that she was needed at home to help look after Angela. I must admit it would have been helpful to have her around to help out with the housework and to care of Titch and to some extent Daniel but we would never have dreamt of her giving up her place at university. I wondered whether her need to be at home was more about her need to be able to see what was happening rather than the need to take on the caring role. Thankfully she found some good friends at university who helped her find ways to cope, but I did feel for her.

The last few months hadn't been easy for Angela and me either. There had been times when IT had really tested our relationship. And I am ashamed to say times when I had really felt like walking away. I wasn't being the husband Angela needed and so I was a failure. She needed somebody who could give her the answers she wanted, someone who could fix the problem. But this bloody problem was just too big for me to fix. We had argued more in the last few months than we had ever done through all our years of being together. Sometimes it was just silly petty things but other times massive big *'well sod you I'm not going to talk to you again'* ones where I could easily have walked out of the house and not gone back.

A lot of the arguments were about finances. I was trying to maintain as much work as I could but was also aware that there were many times when Angela needed me at home with her. My absence from work was not good for the small team I employed or the contractors. Some of them thought that my not being there meant they could cut corners and sometimes just not turn up at all. Then I was getting massive ear-ache from the customers who were understandably not happy. I also started to need to turn work down and that meant there was a lot less money coming in but at the same time we were spending more on heating and food bills. Just silly things like parking charges at the hospital had a big impact on our out-goings. When Angela was having really regular visits to the hospital I joked with the staff about having a season ticket. The nurses didn't quite get my humour. But in reality it was an additional burden which we had just not planned for.

Our relationship altered as IT took hold. I felt as though Angela was becoming more and more distant and would sometimes brush me away when I tried to show any affection. She said that she didn't think she was attractive anymore and that IT was making her into an old woman. At first I tried to reassure her that she was still as gorgeous as ever but as time went on I found it harder and harder to keep telling her when she was adamant that she wasn't going to listen. After a while I just gave up but then she took that to mean that I didn't find her attractive and that I was looking elsewhere for a relationship. That one caused one of the big arguments. I just couldn't reason with her and in the end, very briefly, thought that maybe if she wasn't going to listen I would look around for someone who would listen. There was the woman who worked on the trade counter at the local builder's merchants. She always seemed to give me more attention than the other customers. Maybe she would like a drink. But then the *'my wife doesn't understand me bit'* came to mind and with a jolt I realised that I didn't want another woman, I wanted my Angela. I realised that we needed to re-adjust our relationship to accommodate IT. But after so many years of being together that had not been easy.

But it wasn't all doom and gloom either. Because I was at home so much more it also meant that we were able to spend more time together. On days when Angela was feeling quite well we tried to do things together. Even if it was just going for a walk at the local Country Park or going out into the countryside we tried to make the effort. There were a couple of occasions when we took ourselves off for the day and headed for the coast. They were really special days where we were able to briefly forget about IT and spend some time just being us.

Before I knew it I was at the rugby club. As I walked through the car park I saw Ryan parking his car.

'Nathan, your round I believe Mate' he shouted across to me.

So much for being anxious I thought as I walked over to him. We were picking up our friendship where we had left it, or maybe just a bit before where we left it as this time I was not an emotional wreck. And to his credit, the first thing he talked about was a pint and not IT. Ryan you are a pal.

TWENTY ONE

Rebecca

It wasn't long before Dave, the manager at the museum, offered me more hours in the café. He said that he was impressed with my work and that he wished all the team were as good as me. I was so excited and pleased when he offered me the extra shift. The money I was earning was really making such a difference and also it was great to be meeting so many different people and getting to do new things. I was still generally on the same shift as Dora which was good. We got on really well and were becoming good friends.

Before I left work for the summer holidays, Dave reassured me that there would still be a job for me when I returned to university in September. So when I returned after the long summer break I was able to pick up where I had left off. My first week back at work felt quite strange, I was trying to remember everything I had learnt before the break but it soon came back to me. It was nice to be back; one or two of our regular customers even said that they had missed me and were glad to see me back.

During my first week back Dave asked me if I would mind covering for Dora the following week. She was taking a week's holiday and he wondered whether I would mind doing her job which meant more responsibility, but also a bit more pay. He said that he knew I would be able to do it and that he couldn't think of a better person to ask. I was so excited, what a responsibility and honour.

So there I was, temporarily in charge of the café. Thankfully it was a good week and there were no hitches, I even managed to cash up each night and get the cash register to balance. On my last shift in charge Dave came into the café about half an hour before we were due to close. That was unusual but I just thought he had come because it was my last night in charge. After I had finished my shift he told me how grateful he was and what a great job I had done. He asked if he could take me for a drink to celebrate. I felt a rush of excitement; my boss was so pleased with how I had worked he wanted to take me out for a drink. I accepted his offer, grabbed my coat and bag and met him by the door.

We went to the same pub that Dora and I had gone to when I had first started working at the café. Dave ordered the drinks and then ushered me to one of the small tables for two in the far corner of the pub. He again said how grateful he was to me for all my hard work and what an asset I was to the team. We chatted about general stuff, mainly about work and my family. Dave didn't say much about his family but I seemed to remember Dora telling me that he was married and had got a young son. I didn't feel it was right for me to be asking him about his personal life so kept quiet even though I was curious to know more about him. After about an hour we left the pub, Dave offered to give me a lift back to my room but I declined the offer. I didn't want him to have to go out of his way for me and anyway I thought the walk would do me good. As we left he put his arm on mine and gave it a tight squeeze. I walked back to my room feeling really happy. I'd successfully managed to be in charge of the café for a week and Dave had obviously been really grateful to me for my hard work.

A couple of days later I had a text from Dave *'Hi Rebecca, really enjoyed the drink, maybe we could do it again soon.'* I felt flattered. Dave was obviously really happy with my work. I text back saying that would be nice. The following day I had another text from Dave *'Hi Rebecca, don't suppose you fancy a drink tonight? Dave x.'* Because I hadn't got anything planned I text back saying that if he wasn't busy that would be good, I asked him if we should meet at the same pub. Dave text back saying that he would pick me up at about 7 pm.

At first I wondered how Dave knew my address but then realised that he must have seen it on my application form for the job. So promptly at 7pm Dave pulled up in his car. He greeted me with a big smile and said how lovely I looked. I noticed that Dave seemed to have made an extra effort to look smart. He was wearing casual trousers with a navy checked shirt. I could smell his over powering aftershave which made me feel a bit sick. We drove out of the city and into the countryside. For a brief moment I felt anxious, I didn't know where we were going and it suddenly struck me that nobody knew where I was or who I was with. I looked across to Dave and asked him where we were going. I think he probably heard the rising panic in my voice. He put his hand on my knee and squeezed it 'just a country pub I know, think you will enjoy it they've got a jazz quartet playing, should be a good night.'

With that I began to relax, this wasn't anything sinister; it was just a work colleague taking me out for a drink. But then it did cross my mind why it was me he was taking and not any of the other girls.

The pub was unusually quiet and there were no signs of the quartet. I wondered whether they were gigging later and had not arrived yet. Dave again insisted on buying the drinks. I asked for a lime and lemon but he persuaded me to have a white wine. I accepted because I didn't want to look silly or unsophisticated in front of him, but I really would have preferred a soft drink. I wasn't used to drinking alcohol and wasn't particularly keen on the taste.

Although there were only a handful of other people in the pub, all regulars I suspected, there was a nice cosy feel to it. There was a log fire burning even though it wasn't particularly cold and some quiet music playing in the background. It was an old building, the floor was made from the original stone slabs and there were low oak beams in the ceiling. The furniture was all dark wood and there was a mismatch of chairs at the tables. Two old men stood at the bar with their pints of beer, chatting to the barman. Occasionally they laughed loudly but mainly spoke quietly.

As I drank my wine I slowly began to relax. Dave asked about Mum and seemed genuinely interested and concerned. I had mentioned IT to him just after I had started working at the museum. I thought it was only fair to warn him that if anything happened to Mum I might have to miss my shifts.

I told him about how Mum was and how difficult things were for all of us trying to cope living with IT. I found myself telling him about my fears and worries about the future and my feelings of being torn. In one respect I wanted to be at home to care for her but also I was quite glad that I was away from all the problems. Being at university was almost an escape for me as I was able to get on with life and at times almost forget about Mum. Being some distance from all that was happening meant that I could wrap myself in some delusional belief that everything was okay. I suppose part of my brain was protecting me from having to fully face what was happening. When I had said this to Dave he seemed to understand and appeared to genuinely care about my situation.

More customers arrived in the pub and as they did the noise levels rose. Dave pulled his stool up close so that our knees were touching. Initially I thought he must have done that so we could hear each other speaking but then I began to feel slightly uncomfortable. He leaned closer to me and again the smell of his overpowering aftershave was really quite sickly. Dave started asking about what I had done during the summer holidays. At first his questions were quite broad and were part of the general conversation. I told him about the time away at Granny's and how lovely it had been to be there doing really normal family stuff. I told him how Titch and I had spent a day in the seaside town that was close to Granny's house. We had caught the bus into town and had spent a lovely couple of hours looking in the shops, having an ice-cream on the beach and then having a paddle in the very cold sea. I told Dave how much Titch had enjoyed it and how, because of the job at the museum I had a bit of extra money and had been able to treat her to a new book from the small independent book shop on the High Street. I went on to tell him about what I had been doing with my family during the long holidays and that I had met up with some old friends from school.

As the conversation progressed Dave's questions became more personal and direct. He asked whether I had got a boyfriend and when I said that I hadn't he looked almost pleased. He commented that he couldn't believe that such an attractive young woman wouldn't have boys lining up to date her. As he said this he put his hand on my thigh and briefly began stroking it. I moved my leg away and he stopped but continued to keep his knee touching mine.

I began to feel anxious again. Suddenly this didn't feel like a drink with a colleague. All the conversation had been about me. Dave had not said anything about his family or him, but had kept asking questions about me and my life. It was evident that the jazz quartet was not going to be playing and I began to wonder whether Dave had lied about them. I wasn't sure what Dave was up to but it didn't feel quite right. I didn't know what to do. I didn't think it was appropriate to ask Dave to take me home. What if he miss-read that and thought it was an invitation to go back to my room? But also I knew I didn't want to stay there any longer than I had to. I had a sip of my wine and made my excuses to go to the Ladies. I needed some time to think about what I should do.

When I got back to the table I told Dave that I wasn't feeling very well and asked if we could go home. He looked angry but then reluctantly drank his pint and put the glass down with some force. When we set off back towards the city he was quiet and didn't say anything to me. I could sense that the atmosphere had altered and that he was not happy. As we got closer to home he did start to talk again and seemed his old self. Just before we got back into the city he pulled into a layby and stopped the engine. He leaned across and pulled me towards him and kissed me on the lips. It was awful. My head was spinning and I felt sick. I was petrified about what he was going to do. I pulled away from him and tried to open the car door but he had locked it. In my panic I had forgotten that if I had pulled twice on the handle it would have unlocked. But even if I had been able to get away where would I have gone? We were still some way from home and I would not have been able to out run him. He pulled me back towards him and said that he loved me and wanted to get to know me better.

I really didn't know what to do. When I was at school I had been out with one or two of the boys from my year. It had been nothing serious, just the odd date and a quick kiss when we had been saying our goodbyes but this was a whole different situation. In one respect it felt quite good, someone was taking an interest in me and was telling me how pretty I was but in another it felt wrong. I didn't really know Dave; he was much older than me and I thought he was married. And anyway this was not the way men should treat women.

I realised that for now I had to go along with him. I told him that I really liked him too but that I wanted to get to know him better before we started any kind of relationship. He stroked my face and told me that I was the most beautiful person he had ever seen. For a moment I almost wanted to believe him and to live out this dream of his but I quickly realised that I must not even contemplate his appalling ways. He again kissed me but this time on my cheek. He stroked my hair and looked deep into my eyes.

'I love you, Rebecca, you are everything I have ever dreamed about.'

Thankfully he then started the car and drove me back to my room. As he dropped me off he thanked me for a lovely evening. He then cleared his throat and said that maybe it would be better if I didn't tell anybody that we had been out on a date. With that he kissed me again, on the cheek, and drove off.

I couldn't wait to get into the comparative safety of my room; I rummaged in my handbag to find my keys and fumbled to unlock the main entrance door. Once in my room I stood shaking. What on earth had just happened? How stupid had I been to even contemplate going out for a drink with a stranger? I so wanted to telephone Mum and talk to her but I knew there was no way that I could. Instead I sat on my bed crying and feeling very angry with myself.

I didn't have any more texts from Dave until the day of my next shift. His message read *'Hi Rebecca, hope you are feeling better. Looking forward to seeing you tonight. Let's keep it a secret, love D x.'* I was dreading going back to work, how could I face him and what would I say to him. The only good thing was that Dora was back from her holiday. Reluctantly I set off for my shift feeling very apprehensive.

Dora was already at the café when I arrived. She gave me a hug and said how nice it was to see me again. It was a quiet shift, there were few customers and so we had time to chat in between serving people. I asked Dora about her holiday and she told me all about her few days away visiting family and how lovely it had been to meet up again with her large and extended family. It sounded really good. Dora asked how I was; I think she was picking up that I was quieter than normal. Dave came into the café and acknowledged me and Dora but didn't stay long. I think he was hoping that I was on my own but thankfully Dora was there all the time.

Towards the end of the shift Dora asked if I was okay and how Mum was. She commented that I seemed quiet and preoccupied with my thoughts.

'Are you sure you are okay?' she asked.

I had decided that I wasn't going to tell Dora about Dave. I didn't think she would understand and that she would just think that I had given him the wrong signals and that it was my fault he had tried it on. But as she looked at me with her concerned look I couldn't stop myself. I told her all about him asking me out for a drink and the night at the pub. I didn't go into too much detail about the kisses in the layby but told her enough for her to know how I felt.

Dora listened carefully and when I had blurted out my story she let out a slow, long breath before saying with venom 'the Bastard.' I could tell Dora believed me and that her anger was with Dave. She put her arm round me and gave me hug.

'Let me sort it, I'll have a word with him, he won't bother you again. But if he does you tell me straight away. Do you understand?'

I nodded my head and promptly burst into tears. Dora held me and reassured me that everything would be okay. Once I had stopped crying she told me to get my coat and to go home early. She said that she would soon be away too but not before she had been to see Dave.

I'd not been back at my room long before I got a text from Dora *'Slimy Dave won't be bothering you again. Try not to worry it is all sorted x.'*

I never did find out what Dora had said to Dave. She didn't tell me and I didn't ask her. But after she had spoken to him he kept his distance from me. We spoke when we had to but that was all. I tried to put the memory of that awful night to the back of mind. Had he taken advantage of me? Had he seen that I was vulnerable? How could I have been so bloody stupid?

TWENTY TWO

Angela

It was Tracey's idea to write letters to the children. She had called round to see how I was and over a cup of tea tentatively broached the subject. I think she had probably been testing the water first to see how I was feeling; checking that I was emotionally in a safe enough place to contemplate writing such difficult letters. It was just before my birthday and I had been feeling particularly ill with IT and with the prospect of reaching forty. Most women of my age dread having the 'big' birthday and worry about the significance of reaching forty. For me it was a major milestone as I didn't know whether I would have another one to celebrate.

After Tracey had left, I sat for a long time thinking about what she had said. As always it made utter sense. As she had said it was a legacy to my children, something that they could read and take comfort and advice from. I wasn't sure though. How do you even begin to contemplate writing such a letter? All three children had such different needs and needed me for different reasons. I could feel in my body that time was becoming a precious commodity. I was beginning to feel more ill more of the time and my 'good days' were getting fewer and fewer. I knew it was something I needed to do but where do you begin?

My Darling Rebecca,

I shouldn't be writing this to you, there shouldn't be a need for it, but because of circumstances that I would never have chosen I need to let you know how I feel about you and all my wishes for you. Dear Rebecca, you have given me so much pride and joy, no mother could have as much love for you as I do. Please never forget that.

I remember so clearly the day your Dad and me found out that I was pregnant. We were the happiest people on earth that day. We both cried with joy at the thought of having a baby. You weren't the easiest pregnancy ever, and I think you know that — I've told you often enough! But that does not detract from the love I had for you from the moment I held you. Throughout your life that love has grown, I will never stop loving you.

When I first left you at school it broke my heart, I sobbed after I had left you, a part of me was missing. But once you settled into your routine you started to flourish and enjoyed yourself with your new friends. I loved it when you told me and Dad all your stories about what you had been up to. And through all that you were becoming an accomplished student. I don't know where you got your brains from but all your achievements have made me very proud. Getting into university was such a big moment in our lives. What an achievement, that's my girl. Rebecca I wish I could be with you when you graduate. I should be with you, and you know my love I will be in spirit if not in body. I will be the one that makes the biggest cheer as you step on to the stage to get your award. Make no mistake I will be there.

Rebecca, I want more than anything else for you to be happy. Choose your path carefully but if you make mistakes along the way (and you will) then think carefully about them and move on. Don't ever settle for second best, you deserve the best. And don't feel you have to conform just because that is what is expected of you. Sometimes we have to push the boundaries to get what we want. I know that you have the strength of character to do that. Believe in yourself always and follow your dreams.

Rebecca, I am the proudest mum around, I love you so much and always will.

All my love

Mum xxxx

It took a long time to write the letter to Rebecca and when I had finished I felt emotionally and physically exhausted. As I wrote it tears streamed down my face. There was so much more I wanted to say but didn't know how to begin to articulate it. I didn't write the next two for a few days. I couldn't bring myself to find the energy needed to write such powerful stuff to my children. Writing Rebecca's had been hard enough but how would I begin to write to Daniel and Titch?

I sent Tracey a text saying that I had done Rebecca's. She replied saying that it must have been difficult but that she was proud of me. She added *'one down, two to go'*. That had been one of our shared phrases, whenever things had happened with the children, throughout their childhoods we had used that mantra as our coping strategy. I smiled to myself when I read her text; I knew exactly what she meant.

I thought very carefully about how I would word the letter to Daniel. After his major blip in the Spring I had been additionally vigilant about him and how he was coping. He appeared to have settled back down since the incident with school and the two youths, but I could tell that he was a different boy. The build-up of stress, worry and anger about IT had taken a heavy toll. He was even more guarded in what he shared with us and I could see that he considered things more before he spoke.

Dear Daniel,

This is a letter that I should not be writing to you and I sincerely hope that by some miracle you will never have to read it. If you are reading it I am sure it will be with sadness and anger. But please Daniel, try not to be angry. None of us wanted IT, none of us expected that bombshell to hit our family and none of us wanted things to work out as they have done. You have to believe me when I say I wouldn't do anything to intentionally hurt you.

I was so happy when I gave birth to you — a boy — your Dad and I were so overjoyed. I have always been proud of you, you have achieved so much already and I know that you have a great future ahead of you. I wish I knew for certain that I would be here to see it, but if IT does get the better of me I will be watching over you and will be right by your side.

There are still a lot of things you need to learn about life and about surviving in this big bad world. Listen to your father, I know that might sound like a drag but he only has your best interests at heart and I know he will do his best to help you and support you. Remember that he too was young once!

Daniel, follow your dreams and don't let people tell you that you can't do something.

I love you with all my heart,

Mum xxxx

And finally I had to find the strength to write to Titch. This letter was perhaps the most unfair to write. The other two children were growing up and to some extent didn't need their mum as much, but Titch was different. She was still so young and had got so many hurdles to face. I felt very cheated that I wouldn't be there to guide and support her, but how do I put that in a letter?

Hello Titch, my sweet little darling,

I wish I wasn't writing this to you because it is a very sad thing to have to do. I need to tell you how much I love you and what a special little girl you are to me. You always make me smile and it is always lovely to listen to you when you are playing or telling us your stories.

I am very proud of you. It was the best present ever when I had you. I can remember holding you for the first time and feeling so very lucky that I had got such a beautiful daughter.

There are so many things that I think I should be telling you about. What I really want is for you to grow up a happy girl who is confident. I know that Daddy will help you and also you need to ask Rebecca for help too, she's already gone through a lot of the things that you will have to go through when you are a bit older. Auntie Tracey and Auntie Elspeth will also be there if you need some help.

Sometimes you might feel angry and sad about what has happened. That is normal but you need to talk to someone about it, tell them how you are feeling and don't keep it to yourself. Don't be angry with Daddy, he will be trying his best to look after you; I know he will.

Think hard about what you want to do when you grow up and work towards that at school. Ignore the other children who try and say that you don't need to work hard in your lessons because you do and I want you to try your best always.

Be happy my sweetie, I need you to remember that I will always love you.

Lots of love Mummy xxxx

So there they were written. I felt a complete wreck when I had finished writing them. No mother should be expected to write such letters to her children. I so hoped that maybe I could still get through this and that they would remain hidden in the top drawer of my bedside cabinet until I felt well enough to shred them. But part of me thought that maybe before long Nathan would be giving them to the children and sitting down one at a time with them to read the letters from the grave.

After I had written them I told Nathan what I had done and gave him strict instructions about where he would find them and what he needed to do with them. At first he argued that it was the wrong thing to do and he refused to agree to my request. We argued about it and finally he stormed off, banging the front door as he went. I watched him marching up the cul-de-sac, his hands stuffed deep into his pockets. I wanted to chase after him but I knew it was pointless. His stubbornness was coming through and no amount of discussions would have helped. I knew that he needed to work it through in his own mind. I suppose it was another realisation that maybe we had to face the reality of a future that neither of us wanted to face. Sometimes facing the truth was really difficult.

After an hour or so Nathan came home with a bunch of sorry looking flowers from the local petrol station; his peace offering. He mumbled his apologies and said that he could understand why I had written the letters but that he didn't feel ready to accept that he might have to share them with the children. As I tried my best to arrange the sad looking flowers in the vase we talked about it. We had spent almost a year living with IT and it certainly wasn't getting any easier. There had been some times when there had been a lot of hope and we had both dared to think that the worst was over. But then with cruel twists and turns something else would happen and my beleaguered body would take another blow.

What more could we say to each other, instead we held each other close, sharing a moment of togetherness and shared love. Nathan put his strong arms round me and held me as tightly as he dared. I allowed my body to sink into his and to feel his warmth and love. We stood for a long time saying nothing but sharing so much.

TWENTY THREE

Angela's Mum

Everyone sang to Angela as she blew out the candles on her cake. I had tried to join in but a lump in my throat caught the words and I struggled to make any discernible noise come from my larynx. I looked across at Angela. She looked tired but was, nevertheless, enjoying her birthday celebrations. The social room at the rugby club was festooned with balloons and banners and now on the trestle table there was food debris scattered all over the once white linen table cloth. '*Well*', I thought as I looked at the raft of empty paper plates '*everyone has had a good time*'. Nathan had told me that there wouldn't be much food left but I had still worried whether we had ordered enough.

When Angela was first diagnosed with IT I had insisted that I travel to Yorkshire to stay with the family for a while. I had felt so helpless being at home in Norfolk and needed to see for myself what was happening. On that occasion I had only stayed for a week. I was acutely aware that I did not want to be a burden and that my presence added to the difference that the family was feeling at that time. Initially Daniel and Kitty had thought that I was just visiting; at that stage they had not been told the full facts about Angela's illness. I felt very uneasy because I didn't want to say the wrong thing and so it had been an uncomfortable few days in more than one respect.

Since then I had made a few more trips north to offer practical and emotional support. Each visit bringing with it a deeper sense of helplessness. I felt torn between wanting to be there to support Angela but also being conscious that if it wasn't for IT I wouldn't be there. To me my presence was a constant reminder that family life was so very different. If it wasn't for IT I would have been at home going about my routines and my family would be getting on with life. I spoke to Angela and Nathan about this during my second visit. They were both adamant that they were grateful for the support and that it was helpful. For me it was the only natural thing to do; I had to be with my daughter. During the latest occasion I had been there for just over a month. I needed to go home briefly to sort out things but I also felt that I was needed there.

How does a mother ever reconcile the fact that her daughter is very likely going to die before her? I had struggled with this since I first heard about IT. That wasn't in my plan for my beautiful daughter. It should have been me that was facing death not her. Why was it so utterly unfair? When she was growing up I had such hopes for her. She had been the perfect baby. From very early on she slept at night and gurgled her way through the days. It had been a difficult pregnancy and on doctor's orders I had been practically bedridden for the last two months before she made her appearance. The labour had been long and difficult but as soon as Sister Hetherington, the midwife, had placed her in my arms all that was forgotten.

We had quickly got into a routine and I thoroughly enjoyed every moment of motherhood. Having Angela made my life complete. We were now a family and I was so very content. I sometimes thought back to those days forty years ago. Was it all as lovely as I remembered or with time had my views of life been distorted to paint the perceived idyllic life-style I had created? It had certainly been a good time; I'd got the memories and narratives to support that idea, but I was not sure it was as perfect as I liked to think.

I had worked after leaving school and had continued to do so until Angela was born. In those days it was less common for women to go back to work after having a baby. That was especially true for me as my role as office girl for a firm of solicitors in the local market town was a job and not a career. I had left school with a handful of exams but had never had any aspirations to have a career. My path in life had been mapped out for me by my parents and to some extent the community in which I grew up. The traditional view of women being the home-makers and caring for their family was instilled into me from an early age. I sometimes wondered whether I would have walked a different path if circumstances had been different. But then I thought that I wouldn't have changed a thing. We had had a very happy, secure life. I'd had high expectations for Angela and had always wanted her to do well. As she was growing up I wanted her to experience more in life and have wider opportunities than I had. I had great maternal plans for her to travel the world with her work and to come home regaling us with stories of far off adventures. Within my un-voiced plans I had hoped that she would meet an up and coming business man who would whisk her off her feet. They would marry, have three children and live a comfortable, middle-class life in suburbia. Much as I loved the country life, I had thought that it would stifle Angela's extrovert personality and that she would be more suited to becoming a town dweller.

I must admit that when Angela started showing increasing interest in Nathan I was a bit disappointed. He didn't quite fit into my plans. He was a lovely young man, always very polite when we met him and seemed besotted with Angela but he wasn't the business man I had envisaged. His appearance was the first thing that helped blur my appraisal of him. He had long, jet black hair and seemed permanently attached to an old leather biker jacket that he wore constantly. He was clean and tidy in his appearance apart from the loutish hair and jacket. When we first met he had just officially left school, although I understood that he had not been the most regular attendee. He had left with no qualifications and hadn't got a job and was unsure where he wanted to go. However, good fortune had prevailed and he had been offered a temporary job with 'Uncle Bob'. Bob was a close friend of the Williamson's family. He was a builder with a good reputation locally. My understanding was that Bob had offered to take Nathan on briefly as a favour to Nathan's mother. I suspect he wasn't sure whether the young lad would be able to cope with the discipline required or whether he had the commitment to knuckle down to work. However, this opportunity had been the making of Nathan. He had seized every opportunity given to him and rose to every challenge that Bob put in his way. Within the six months of his temporary post he had impressed Bob sufficiently to be offered a permanent position. I suppose it was an unofficial apprenticeship. Nathan certainly had a very good mentor and teacher in Bob and, to his credit, worked very hard to develop his skills and knowledge.

As Nathan's and Angela's relationship developed I watched him grow into a hard-working and dedicated young man and realised that my initial worries and doubts had been unfounded. I began to realise that although he wasn't the white-collar business man I had in mind as suitable son-in-law material he nevertheless was the right person for Angela. And to his credit, quite soon after starting to go out with her he had his hair cut into a style more befitting a future son-in-law of mine. As he said with a twinkle in his eyes 'you can take the boy out of rock and roll but you can't take the rock and roll out of the boy.'

Rebecca came over to me and draped her arm around my shoulder. 'Hiya Gran' she said 'good party?'

I nodded my head in agreement, 'yes it looks as though everyone is having a good time; have you had enough to eat?'

Rebecca groaned 'oh Gran stop worrying, I've eaten plenty thank you, although party sausage rolls aren't really my thing now.'

'You university types are all the same' I said with a grin as I squeezed her arm. 'Is it getting any better?' I asked.

'Oh you know it's okay really. Sometimes I really want to be back here so that I can see Mum and see for myself how she is. I don't think she always tells me the truth when we speak on the phone, and Dad isn't much better. It wasn't easy going back in September but once I got back into the swing of things it was okay, and I knew I would be back for the party.'

Rebecca's tone suggested a deep pain but I decided it was better not to pursue it at the moment. Standing in a room full of people celebrating her mother's fortieth wasn't the time or place to take this conversation any further.

Another jolt to my conscious thought; my daughter's fortieth birthday, would she be here to celebrate her forty first I wondered bitterly to myself.

I desperately wanted to ask Rebecca if she had been told the latest news about Angela's prognosis. I guessed that Angela and Nathan had not said anything as they had only heard the news the previous Monday and I think it was still sinking in. I knew that the younger two hadn't been told. Angela had told me that they had decided they would wait until after the party to tell them. I was relieved that they had decided to be honest with the children. With the body-blow that we had received on Monday they really needed to start preparing for the worst.

I looked over and saw Kitty playing with some other young children. They had found a rogue balloon and were playing handball with it across the room. Kitty looked so young and happy, and briefly like the Kitty I knew and loved. I think of all the children it was Kitty that I worried about the most. She now knew that Angela was seriously ill and was, understandably, really struggling to come to terms with everything. She had changed beyond belief since I waved her off after the Christmas break last year. Her ubiquitous smile had faded and there were times now where she looked dejected and as though she was carrying a heavy weight of burden. I wasn't sure whether it was easier for her when she surmised that something was wrong but hadn't been sure. At least then she had been able to drift in and out of the worry and had brief periods where she managed really well. But then she had started to ask questions. Her behaviour changed noticeably at home and school and she became increasingly unhappy. She had started to get into trouble at school more and more and was having more arguments with Daniel too.

Kitty had guessed that Angela was ill soon after she was diagnosed but had not said anything. Instead she had quietly watched from the side-lines, carefully observing what was happening within her family. Everything came to head in April when I was staying with the family. Nathan had gone to watch the rugby with Ryan. He hadn't particularly wanted to go because of leaving Angela but because I was there he reluctantly went out for the evening. It was the last match of the season and so it felt right and proper that he should go. When he came home he was very distressed. I think the pent up emotions had finally been released and he had allowed himself to share his feelings with Ryan. Kitty must have overheard some of the conversation between Angela and Nathan when he had come in. The following morning she had feigned a tummy ache and had not gone into school. That was when she asked Angela whether she was going to die.

When Angela told me about the conversation my heart died a little more. The pain and anguish on Angela's face was hard to bear, coupled with the knowledge that Kitty was now party to the information that Angela and Nathan had tried so hard to hide from her.

Part of me felt utter relief that Kitty was being included in the awful family saga. I had fretted constantly about whether they should tell her. Part of me thought that she was too young and that she didn't need to know, but the logical half of me thought that she really needed to know and that she had a right to know what was happening. I reasoned that Kitty was a bright girl and that she would soon guess that something was wrong. In my despair I had been to speak to the minister from our local church. I didn't attend church regularly but knew the minister quite well. I felt I could explore with him in a safe place my feelings and anxieties. I made him aware that I was not asking for his prayers for a cure, but that I would appreciate his sage thoughts. I think more than anything I wanted to speak to someone who knew me but who wasn't a friend. Someone who would not judge me and who would listen without putting their values on me.

We sat for a long time in the sitting room of his manse. I noticed how orderly the room was, furnished in pastel tones that provided a calming effect. I wondered whether the choice of paint and decorations had been deliberate. A carefully thought through example of his ministry. The old clock on the mantel piece methodically chimed the hour and half hour, slowly measuring time. But while I was sitting there, time was irrelevant. I needed the space to explore what was happening to my family, and the minister, in his tidy, still room offered that space.

I think the conversation had initially been quite disjointed. I tried to tell him all that was happening in an ordered, chronological way but as intrusive thoughts entered my brain they tumbled out with little sequence and at times were incoherent as I tried to share my story.

I was angry; I didn't want to share my story with anyone. While it was in my heart it was relatively obscure and I was secure because there was no public knowledge of the awful events that were unfolding within my family. While the story was ours and not out there for the world to know we had just a little control. But when I realised that the secrecy was not healthy and that it was creating all sorts of sadness I knew I had to talk to Rev. Johnstone.

Rev. Johnstone listened carefully and made no comment until I had poured out my heart. He acknowledged that it must be a difficult period for me and my family and then gently and sensitively began to ask about IT and how each member of the family was coping. He spoke quietly and I could tell he was very carefully selecting the words to use with great consideration and deliberation. He spoke about the children and the need to respect them. Within that he suggested that all three children would know that there was something wrong with Angela. He spoke about how children were more aware of what was happening around them than adults might think. He said that in his experience he thought that they would all be observing what was happening and would be seeing all the changes that were occurring in the family. He said it would be likely that they would have noticed that Angela was looking tired and ill, that she was often going to the hospital and that she was off sick from work. He said that they would know that Nathan wasn't going to work as often and that I was staying with them more regularly than normal.

He spoke about ripples on a pond and likened Angela to the central ripple and how each other ripple represented the family and then friends and the community. He didn't need to say to me that by not sharing information with the children we were being disrespectful to their intelligence and that we were denying them the opportunity to be included in something that they needed to be included in. He didn't need to say that it was our responsibility to give them choice and to offer sufficient information for them to make the choice about how much more information they wanted. He didn't need to say that these were going to be the most difficult conversations we would ever have as a family. He didn't need to say that I had a duty as a mother and grandmother to support Angela through this.

The clock on the mantel piece broke the silence as it chimed out the half-hour. The clock was the only noise I could hear. Outside there was silence, the world was briefly silent. It reflected the weight in my heart and the burden on my soul.

As Rev. Johnstone was speaking I thought about Kitty, Daniel and Rebecca. They were all intelligent children and were always very observant of their surroundings. That, I thought, was a trait inherited from their maternal Grandpa.

Angela's father was a naturalist and had a keen eye and ear for all that was happening in the surrounding countryside. His knowledge of country lore had been acquired not through books but from observing nature and making detailed notes of his observations. Surely, just as he would recognise changes in the seasons and animals' behaviour so too would the children observe changes within their family.

I had left Rev. Johnstone with mixed emotions. I felt unusually peaceful and calm having shared my burden with someone who was prepared to listen and who didn't rush me. Rev. Johnstone had not judged my family for their behaviour nor had he told me what I should do. Instead he had shared his thoughts with humility and grace. But as one burden had been lifted so another weighed down on my shoulders. With the greater understanding that I had acquired from the minister I was aware that I needed to share some of the discussion with Angela and Nathan and help them to understand the importance of talking to the children. It was evident what I needed to do, however, what was not so clear was how I was going to do it.

* * *

A loud bang brought me out of my contemplations. I looked across the room and saw that the red balloon had burst, shards of red rubber gently floating to the floor to meet the already fallen pieces. Kitty, after the initial shock of the bang looked crestfallen that the game was evidently over. The previous enjoyment quickly dissipating into sadness and rejection. A combination of being over-excited about the party, being tired after a busy family day and the shadow of concern that was always at the back of her mind acting like a heady cocktail descending her into a sad place again. The bursting of the balloon had been a trigger and now Kitty was standing in the middle of the dance floor crying. I ran over to her and, with an arm around her shoulder took her to one side and sat her on my knee. Angela was quickly over by our side. I again noticed how drawn and tired she looked.

'I think it might be time we made our leave' I said to Angela, 'we've all had a busy day and it is getting late.'

Angela gave me a grateful nod. I suspect Kitty's sadness was the excuse Angela had been waiting for. She could now slip away from the party and use Kitty's tears as the reason.

Neither Daniel nor Rebecca put up any kind of protest and both helped get together all our belongings. Angela and Nathan said their thank yous and goodbyes and we made a swift exit from the rugby club social room. The party was in full swing and I suspected it would carry on for a while yet, certainly until the bar closed. As I looked back into the melee of bodies swaying on the dance floor I again spotted the empty trestle tables. I gave a silent thank you to Big Billy for helping to arrange the party. When he had heard that it was Angela's birthday he had spoken to Ryan about arranging a surprise party for her. Ryan had talked it through with Nathan and they had agreed that a party would be lovely but Nathan asked that it was not a surprise one. He thought that it would be more appropriate for Angela to know what was happening. Once it had been agreed Big Billy took charge of the planning. This included him organising a raffle to raise some money towards the cost of the catering, and I understood that he had managed to negotiate a very favourable price for the hire of the room.

As we left the room I could see Big Billy strutting his stuff on the dance floor. I was so grateful to him for all he had done, but at that moment my main gratitude was that I wasn't going to have to tidy up the room and do all the washing up. I couldn't have faced that. All I wanted was a cup of tea and sleep.

It was late when we got back to the house. Kitty had nodded off in the car and so it was a case of a quick face wash and brushing of teeth and bed. She put up no complaints but before she did climb into her bed I spotted her giving Angela an extra big cuddle 'I love you Mummy' she said in her tired voice 'happy birthday.'

I must admit I wasn't late following Kitty into bed. I was tired but found that I could not go to sleep. A hundred and one thoughts were scurrying round in my mind. There was a common thread to all of them; my beautiful forty year daughter was now seriously ill and any hope of a cure was looking increasingly unlikely. Tears of pity, anger and sadness rolled down my cheeks as I silently wept at the unfairness of it all. I also knew that now the party was over there was going to have to be the most heart wrenching of conversations with the children.

TWENTY FOUR

Angela

I put the phone down after speaking to Mum and a huge sense of childlike excitement swept over me. For a few weeks our Christmas had been hanging in the balance. After I had received the news that things with IT weren't looking good the whole family had been in a tailspin. Nathan and I had decided that we were at the point where we were going to have to prepare the children for the worst. All three of them knew that I was ill and that it was potentially serious, but after my birthday party we had sat them down together to tell them that things were getting a little less hopeful.

The look on all their faces will be etched into my mind for ever. They all sat in silence for a few minutes as they tried to comprehend what we had told them. Nathan and I had promised each other that we would not cry and that we would be strong for them. Before we told them, we had carefully rehearsed what we were going to say. I was dreading it. I had thought about the possibility of having to tell them for months but had hoped against hope that maybe we would be saved from having to. It was difficult enough telling them that I was ill but telling them that maybe I might die was just too difficult to contemplate. The nagging, persistent thought had kept coming into my mind that it was so utterly unfair and something that no mother should ever have to do. Nobody prepares you for this kind of conversation; you are on your own, sink or swim.

So on that cold Sunday in November we faced one of the biggest challenges that IT had thrown at us to date. When Nathan and I had been rehearsing what we were going to say we'd gone through a hundred and one different scenarios. I think the most difficult bit was how to introduce the topic.

'Hi kids, come and sit down, Mum and Dad have got something to say to you...'

Or

'Mum and Dad have got some news for you, are you sitting comfortably...?'

Do you just blurt it out and wait for the fallout or do you build it up slowly? We agreed that we should start with some introductory bit about how they knew that I was not well and that the doctors had been working really hard to make IT go away but that now they were worried that maybe IT wasn't playing ball. We decided that it should be me who told the children and that Nathan would take on the supporting role. It was still really hard but at least with our script to support us we managed to fumble our way through it, although I don't think either of us would win any Oscars for our performance. And I know that neither of us ever wanted to have to have such a conversation again.

Once again I was so grateful to Nathan for being my rock. I knew how much IT had taken a toll on him but apart from the odd few blips he had been the strong one. He had been the one there for me throughout the awful year. He had been the one to hold me close and to give me strength to carry on when I had questioned whether there was any point in carrying on. He had held the family together. He was there for me and the children as they sat trying to understand what we had told them.

Mum had deliberately stayed out of the way; she knew of our plans and so had suggested that she would make her excuses and go out while we told the children. She had asked whether we wanted her to be there but we felt it was better if it was just me and Nathan. Somehow it didn't seem right that Mum was there at that time. She'd be there later to help pick up the pieces.

It was Titch who broke the silence after I had finished telling them.

Neither Nathan nor I had been quite prepared for her question. She showed no real emotion but asked quietly whether it was because she had burst the balloon at the party the night before. Nathan and I looked at each with surprise, how the hell do you answer that one?

I asked Titch what she meant; I was struggling to understand where her logic was coming from. She said that when the balloon had burst it had made a loud bang and so she thought that it must have caused IT to get worse and that was why I might not get better.

It dawned on me that she probably really believed that there was some relationship between the balloon popping and IT. Was that how young children saw the world I wondered? Maybe all through the illness she had been harbouring fears that something she had done was the cause of IT. I vaguely remembered reading something in a magazine at the hairdressers about how young children don't think like adults and how they make illogical mistakes. It was ages ago when I had read this, long before I was in such a situation. I remember flicking through the magazine while I waited for my appointment. I'd not really taken much notice of the article, being more interested in the latest gossip about one of the infamous footballer's wives who was regularly making the headlines at that time. I was now annoyed with myself for being more interested in some salacious gossip instead of something that might actually have relevance.

I tried my best to reassure Titch that no it was nothing to do with the balloon, but I wasn't sure I had managed to convince her. She didn't say anymore, she just sat holding Rebecca's hand as tightly as she could, listening to the other two expressing their feelings. I could see her biting the corner of her lip; a habit she had when she was nervous or distressed.

It was Rebecca who spoke next. She wanted to know more details about what we meant and about what the hospital was doing to help. She was adamant that she was not going to go back to university and that she would stay and look after me. Nathan and I had sort of expected that response and so both argued that she needed to go back to complete the term. We promised that we would keep her informed and that if anything changed we would let her know. She didn't say much more, instead she held onto Titch's little hand.

Daniel didn't say much. I could see he was trying hard to hide his emotions from us. Since the incident earlier in the year he had been very careful to keep his feelings deep inside him. Nathan had tried to talk to him and had encouraged him to share his feelings but he had always avoided talking about IT. He did, a few months ago say to me that he wished Nathan would not talk to him about what was happening. He told me that he knew what was happening but didn't want to share his feelings. When I asked why, he became defensive and shouted that it was because he needed to stay in control. With that he had stormed out of the kitchen, banging the door behind him. So much for being in control I thought to myself with an ironic smile.

All three children were quiet for the rest of that dark, miserable Sunday. None of us particularly felt like eating and there was an uncomfortable atmosphere in the house. After we had convinced Rebecca that she should go back to university she went to her room. I left her for a while, giving her some space to think through the implications of the news. I wasn't sure what I could say to her; there was nothing I could say that was going to make things any better. I had just told her that I might die so what words of comfort or hope could I possibly offer. I asked Mum if she would mind going to speak to her. I thought that maybe Granny would be a better option than a useless mother who was letting her children down in one big style.

Mum, with her usual knack of knowing the right words at the right time spent some time with Rebecca in her bedroom. I think she had probably done more listening than talking but I knew it had helped. Rebecca emerged from her room with very red, blotchy eyes. For a moment I again saw the five year Rebecca standing crying in the classroom as I left her. How could I leave her again? How could IT be so cruel? As I looked at her, I knew with clarity what I had to do. I wasn't ready to leave my children and my family. IT wasn't going to get the better of me. I knew that eventually IT would take over my life but for now it was going to be me who was in control.

* * *

Within the few seconds of looking at Rebecca and remembering her as a little girl on her first day at school I resolved that I would not give in. As the year with IT had passed I had started to lose some of my strength to cope, I had allowed doubt into my mind and I was slowly allowing IT to take control. I knew I had to stop this, I didn't want to stare death in the face, it was already breathing down my neck but I wasn't ready to step off this stage just yet.

The following morning I telephoned the GPs surgery and asked for an appointment. I was in luck; there was an available slot on the Wednesday at 4pm. My appointment was with a GP that I had not previously met, she was a locum standing in for one of the older members of the team. I explained to her about the consultation with Mr Gough and the fear that IT was becoming more aggressive and taking over my body. She listened with consideration and then took time to read my notes. She acknowledged that physically things were not where they would hope but she then asked about my emotional state. I explained that I had good support from my family, especially Nathan and my Mum and that I had two good friends in particular who were always there for me. She asked whether I would like to make another appointment to see her as she wanted to talk more about what was happening. Although it was a quick consultation, I left feeling as though someone had taken the time to try and understand what I was feeling. I made the appointment for the following Monday afternoon.

It was a difficult few days before the appointment. The news of IT still hanging heavily over the house. To make things worse, Mum had to return home, she had got things arranged which would have been difficult to rearrange and so although she said she would stay to help with the children I insisted that she went back down south. It was hard watching her drive away; I felt that I was losing one of my supports but also the realisation that she wasn't getting any younger and the worry about me must have been affecting her. I also knew she wasn't the bravest of drivers anymore and suspected that she did not relish the long drive between our houses.

So the house became very quiet; Rebecca was back at university, Mum was back home and Titch and Daniel were unusually subdued. Neither of them had said much after we had told them about IT. Following Titch's unexpected question about the balloon she had not really said much. I could tell that she was carefully thinking about the news but there were also periods when she seemed to be getting on with life. It was difficult to decide whether she was quiet because of the news or because of Rebecca's return to university. She still hadn't got used to her big sister being away and cherished the times when she came home. On the Monday as Titch was getting ready to go to school, I heard Rebecca saying her goodbyes and promising that it would not be long before she would be home for the big Christmas holiday. I think that seemed to satisfy Titch and she set off for school feeling reassured that her big sister would be home quite soon.

Daniel had agreed to walk Titch round to her school; it was on the way to his and sometimes, reluctantly he would drop her off for us. I don't think it was seen as being that cool for a fourteen year old to be out with his little sister, but with good grace he did his dutiful role. As soon as they had reached the top of the cul-de-sac I telephoned Titch's school and asked to speak to the head teacher. Mrs Beaumont was aware of the situation at home and had been additionally vigilant of Titch's needs since she found out about IT. I wanted her to be aware that it had been an emotional weekend and that we had given Titch some difficult news about the progress of IT. She reassured me that she would alert Titch's class teacher and that they would 'keep an eye out' for me.

The following Monday I kept my appointment with the GP and was pleased that I had. She took the lead during the consultation and did more talking than listening this time. She spoke about how IT inevitably affects patients physically but she said that there were also emotional implications that sometimes were overlooked by the medics. She alluded to them sometimes being guilty of seeing the illness in a neatly contained box without thinking about some of the other parts of a patient's life. She spoke about how the physical side effects would filter out to affect all aspects of the patient's life, including family life. I looked at her with a puzzled expression 'what do you mean?'

'Well' she said trying to put into layman's terms what she was thinking 'if you think of your life as being a jigsaw with all the different pieces making up the complete you, you can see how if one or two pieces are taken out your life suddenly becomes incomplete. When you were given the news about IT I imagine it was not just your health that was taking a pounding. In my experience it is all the bits of your life, your family, your work, your relationship with your partner and your friends, everything, it all gets caught up in the illness. And when that happens it is difficult for you to manage everything as you did before.'

She stopped briefly and looked at me. 'Getting a diagnosis like IT affects people in different ways, but one thing that generally happens is that the patient suddenly has to cope with lots and lots of different emotions. I am sure you had loads of questions and thoughts about the news. The news is like having a sledgehammer knocking on your life. Suddenly everything that you took for granted is changing and within it all you feel out of control. I think that the actual illness is only part of the problem. Patients have to suddenly cope with loads of other issues too and for that they need some support.'

What she was saying seemed to make utter sense, why hadn't I thought of it like that before, and more importantly why the hell hadn't someone else spoken to me like this before? I thought back to the nurse who sat in when I first met Mr Gough and he gave me the diagnosis. I had looked to her pleading for some answers or reassurance. I remember how she just moved uncomfortably in her seat without offering anything. Why hadn't she or one of Mr Gough's other colleagues sat me down then and said this to me. Maybe I wouldn't have been ready to hear that then, there was so much going on and so much to take in, but if only they had taken the time to talk to me, to explain all the emotional and social crap that I was going to have thrown at me, maybe then I could have coped a bit better with everything.

I thanked the GP for her time and kindness. It probably wasn't appropriate, and I didn't, but I could have given her big hug. She had helped me to see things in a different light. She hadn't promised a miracle cure and she hadn't given me unrealistic hope that everything would be okay, but what she did do was help me to see things from a very different perspective.

I left the surgery with a new spring in my step; there was a lot to think about from what she had said and I needed some time to think things through, but she had given me some hope and a sense of control that I had not had before. What she had said made utter sense. Of course IT was going to impact on everything in my life, it was going to put me in a different emotional place and see the world differently but I was still me. I was still Nathan's wife and the children's mother.

The conversation with the GP was a bit of a turning point. It had offered me a better understanding of what was happening to me. I think that and the shock of the news that the medics were beginning to wonder what they could do next to help me was the jolt I needed. I wasn't ready to leave my children, I wasn't going anywhere for as long as I could manage.

The new, aware me started to think differently. I was not going to allow IT to make me into a patient; I was going to control IT not the other way round. As I changed my mind-set I began to feel more positive about everything. Whereas I had been dreading Christmas and had anticipated it being spent at home with everyone feeling grumpy I now could see it being a happy time and a special time for the children, just as it always had been. With each passing day, following my visit to the GP I had pushed myself a little bit harder. I started trying to go for a short walk each day and if I didn't feel like that I would make sure I did some physical housework. The effect was positive and slowly I started to feel better in myself. I kept telling myself I was in control and quietly but firmly kept telling IT to bugger off.

I even booked an appointment with my hairdresser and instead of a quick trim had a proper wash, cut and blow. It had been months since I had felt like taking the time to have a proper cut, generally plumping for the quickest and easiest option. I'd not been able to face the inevitable conversations with Chris my hairdresser. Before IT I was a regular customer, I couldn't bear it when my hair began to lose its style so always made sure I was there every six weeks. Chris and I used to talk about life and our respective families and what we were planning for tea and all the other mundane conversations that happen up and down the country in hairdressers every day. But suddenly with the arrival of IT I couldn't face all that chit chat. I didn't want Chris to be the one who told me that my hair was not in such good condition or that it was getting thinner each time I went for a cut. But the new reinvigorated me took the plunge and made an appointment. The whole experience was lovely. I felt as though I was being pampered and as Chris styled my dishevelled mop back into style, I closed my eyes and wandered off into a happy place.

Just that little treat made me feel so different. I was suddenly Angela again and not someone with IT. When Nathan saw my new hairdo he couldn't quite believe his eyes. He said it made me look so much better which of course it did. That compliment then drew me back to my make-up bag. I'd not bothered with my make up since about Easter when the faff of spending time making myself attractive seemed to be a pointless activity. For a while, make-up just wasn't important, it wasn't going to mask IT and it was no longer a barrier that I could hide behind. It seemed a waste of time pretending that I was attractive and that make-up would enhance my features. But after my session with Chris I decided that perhaps I could make the effort again and that I was worth it.

With this new Angela in mind I decided that I needed to buy new make-up. Psychologically I thought I needed new and with that excuse I telephoned Tracey to see if she fancied meeting me in town for a coffee, catch up and shop.

We met at our usual café; I deliberately got there early. I wanted to be there when Tracey arrived; not being on time had become a feature of my life. Over the last year I had been getting slower and slower. Maybe that was a feature of IT and the physical side effects or maybe, following on from my conversation with the GP it was a combination of the physical and the emotional. Maybe ITs insidious fingers had wrapped themselves so tightly round my mind that I thought lateness had become part of my identity. Whatever, the reason, I was determined I was not going to be late for my trip out with Tracey. She too took a double take when she walked in and saw me sitting at our usual table.

'Hello Ange, you look amazing, look at the new hairdo, it looks good.'

We gave each other a quick hug 'the usual?' I asked, half knowing the answer.

'Yes please, but it's my turn.'

'Not today, it's my turn and don't argue.'

I returned to the table with a skinny latte for Tracey and a pot of tea for me.

'Well, look at you; you're looking really well, how are you feeling?'

Tracey was aware of the news from the consultant and so the *'I've really made an effort look'* was a bit of a surprise. I told her about seeing Rebecca looking so forlorn after we had told the children about the prognosis and how that had been the kick that I had needed.

'Oh heck that must have been difficult' was her only comment.

Tracey groaned when I told her about the conversation with the GP and how she had helped me see things from a different perspective.

'Why the hell didn't somebody sit you down at the start of all this crap and tell you that?' she asked with annoyance. 'You're not the only person going through this, why isn't there some support in place. It isn't really rocket science is it?' She spoke with passion and I could see the cogs whirring. She sipped her latte and for a moment was somewhere far away in the land of planning.

I watched her over the rim of my tea cup, *'what's she planning now'* I thought to myself, knowing full well that she had some master plan developing in her mind. She didn't say anymore but I got the feeling that wouldn't be the end of her protestations.

After our coffee we headed for the department store where Rebecca and I had gone to buy the dress for her interview. I thought back to that Saturday morning and what a lovely time we had had together. That shopping trip had been a bit of a first for me. It was the first time we had been shopping as two adults instead of mother and daughter. I suppose thinking back last Christmas had been a turning point for Rebecca, she had grown up very quickly when she heard about IT. Because of that she had lost some of her innocence but also we had grown in our relationship.

Tracey and I headed for the cosmetics section; our sense of smell being bombarded with lots of different aromas as we walked there. I looked at the sales assistants who were all made up perfectly. I noticed how they were all incredibly young looking and stick thin. I wondered whether part of the essential criteria on the job description was that prospective candidates must have flawless skin, healthy long hair and be a single digit dress size. I felt that one or two of them were looking at me with some sort of disdain because of my lack of make-up. But then I decided that I was paranoid and thought it best to ignore them. If they'd been through what I'd been through then they too might need some SOS make-up.

I had planned to buy a new lipstick and foundation but was also tempted with an eye-liner and mascara too. The deed didn't take long, I knew which brand I wanted and also had a good idea about the colours that would make me the happiest, including a bright red lipstick. Tracey smiled as I was paying for my goods.

'I just knew you'd go for red lippy, you scarlet woman' she teased.

After I'd paid for my purchases and my new treasures had been handed over to me, Tracey put her arm through mine and steered me towards the underwear department.

'Come on Scarlet, time we got you some decent knickers again.'

I tried, unconvincingly, to protest that I didn't need new underwear, but she was not having any of it.

'The new Angie deserves some new undies' she said and quickly followed it up 'my Christmas present to you.'

And so within less than half an hour I had new make-up and new underwear. My retail therapy was certainly working.

After our shopping we had another drink before Tracey had to head off to do something at home.

'So what are planning to do at Christmas, back to your Mum's as usual?' she asked.

'Not really sure' was the best I could manage as an answer. 'We've not really thought about it this year with everything else. I didn't think I would be fit to go so we've sort of just let it pass by.'

'But Ange, you always go, it's part of the children's life, you can't not go, especially as you are feeling a bit better at the moment. Anyway apart from having to sit in the car once you get there you won't need to do much will you? And I know your Mum would be so happy if you were there with her. It is important to her isn't it?'

She was right really what was stopping us. Christmas had been a bit of an elephant in the room this year. The children normally started talking about it straight after my birthday and planning what we were going to do. In years gone by there had been an anticipated buzz of excitement from them as they counted down the days to going to Granny's. But this year Daniel and Titch had both been very quiet about the subject. It hadn't really crossed my mind until now, but maybe they were being reticent because of IT. Once again the bloody thing was getting in the way of family life. Yes the GP was right.

A slow smile spread across my face 'Tracey, you are right, oh bloody hell, Christmas is back on for the Williamsons.' I said with genuine excitement.

Tracey gave me a hug, 'must dash but will speak soon and see you before you go.'

And with that she was heading back towards where I guessed she would have parked her car. I headed back home with a million and one thoughts running through my head. Of course we were going to celebrate Christmas; it was going to be business as usual for us. I couldn't wait to tell Nathan and the children and to ring Mum.

I started walking to the bus stop but stopped myself. Instead I turned heel and headed back towards the shops. I stopped off at the newsagents and bought three Advent calendars. I knew Rebecca wouldn't be home initially to open hers each day but thought that Nathan and I could do it for her until she arrived home.

TWENTY FIVE

Titch

Daniel was waiting for me at the school gates like he had promised. As I walked out from my class room I could see him standing with his back to the wind. He had got his big black jacket on and had pulled the hood up over his head. He looked really funny because he'd scrunched his shoulders up to try and keep warm and it made him look like he hadn't got a neck. I could see that he'd got his school bag over his shoulder and his hands were in his pockets. He was kicking some leaves that had fallen from the sycamore tree that was next to the school gate.

When I got up close to him he straightened his neck and looked more normal.

'Hello Trouble' he said as I walked towards him. I liked it when he called me different names; it always made me feel special.

'Button your coat up Twit it's cold.'

Daniel held my bag while I struggled with the zip on my coat. It wasn't a good zip and I always had trouble fastening it.

'Come on, it's cold' he repeated.

'I know it is, but I can't do it.'

After another couple of goes I managed it. Daniel carried on holding my bag for me.

'So Titch, what kind of day have you had?' he asked.

'I've got a secret' I said proudly.

'Are you going to tell me or do I need to tickle it out of you?'

'No, can't tell you, need to tell Mum and Dad first.'

Daniel pretended to start tickling me but I dodged him and started running up the road.

'Titch wait' he shouted running after me.

He caught up with me and got hold of my hand like I was a baby.

'Don't run off like that, we are too close to the road and there are lots of cars parked picking kids up.'

'Sorry Daniel.'

'So apart from the big secret, what have you done?'

'Well we were supposed to have PE today but didn't because some men were testing the fire alarms in the hall so instead Miss let us do some painting. I did a picture with Sally and we stuck loads of glitter on it, it was good fun.'

'Was that it all day? Didn't you do any lessons?'

'Of course we did Silly, we did maths and English and geography.'

'Wow busy day then.'

By the time I had told Daniel what lessons I had had we were nearly home. We could see Dad's van was on the drive which meant he was home. The lights were on in the room but Mum must have closed the curtains because I couldn't see in to the house. Daniel got his key out to unlock the door.

'Mum, we're home' I shouted 'and I've got something exciting to tell you.'

Mum came into the hallway 'and I've got something exciting to tell you two too.'

Daniel looked at Mum, 'Please let her go first she's been driving me mad all the way home saying that she has got a secret, the suspense is killing me.'

'I need to tell you and Dad' I said trying to sound important.

'Nathan, Titch has got some important news' Mum shouted into the kitchen.

Dad came in holding the kitchen towel. 'Hello you two, had a good day?'

'Well' said Mum, 'don't keep us in suspense.'

'Well, guess what, this morning Mrs Rigsby said that she was getting ready for Christmas and that she had been thinking about the Christmas service at school. She wants me to be an angel in the Christingle service. I'm going to have to talk in front of everyone in the school and all the mums and dads.'

'Titch that is brilliant news, you clever girl' said Mum.

'Way to go Titch, a star' said Dad, 'when is your performance, we want front row seats.'

'Nice one Titch' said Daniel, 'you need to tell Rebecca that one.'

'Well' said Mum 'two lots of news in one day.'

'So what's your news Mum?' I asked.

I was suddenly worried because every time Mum had news it was always about IT and it was always horrible things. I looked towards Dad but could tell that he didn't look worried. Maybe it was not something horrible.

'Well' said Mum, 'maybe we need to sit down first.'

My heart sank. It was going to be bad news, I just knew it. Suddenly I felt really sad and wasn't bothered that I was going to be in the stupid Christmas play anyway.

'Well' said Mum again, 'this morning I met Auntie Tracey for coffee in town and we got talking and she was asking me about Christmas. I told her that because of me being poorly we hadn't talked about it and that maybe we would stay at home and that with a bit of luck Granny would come to us for a change. But then Auntie Tracey said that I was being silly and that we should go to Granny's as usual. So I spoke to your Dad and then I telephoned Granny and guess what?'

'Does that mean we are going to Granny's' I shouted.

'It sure does my little Christmas Angel'.

Mum and Dad looked at each other and started laughing.

'We're going to Granny's, we're going to Granny's' I shouted as I ran over to Mum and gave her a cuddle, 'are we really going?'

Mum nodded and started laughing.

'So can I write my letter to Santa?' I asked. I'd not written my letter because I thought that Father Christmas might not come because of Mum being poorly.

'Of course you can, I'm sure he'll be waiting for it.'

'But Neil Ross said that Father Christmas wouldn't come to our house because you were poorly.'

Neil Ross was one of the big boys in school and sometimes he said nasty things to me about Mum being poorly. I hadn't told anybody about him because I was scared that what he was saying was true. But then without thinking about it I had said about him being nasty to me.

'He did, did he?' said Mum, 'Mmm well I reckon that Father Christmas won't be going to his house on Christmas Eve. Father Christmas only goes to visit nice boys and girls who have been good. It is clear to me that Neil Ross certainly hasn't been good this year. By the way, which class is he in?'

I wasn't sure which class he was in and I was now worried that Mum would say something at school and he would get into trouble and then he would be even more horrible to me.

'I know Neil Ross' said Daniel, 'his big brother is in my form class, nobody likes him he's a …'

'Daniel, it's okay thank you we can guess what kind of person he is' warned Dad as Daniel was just about to say something rude about him.

'Well' said Mum changing the subject. 'I don't think we need to worry about him just now do we? But Titch, if he says anything else to you please let me know Sweetheart won't you? Right you two, go and get your school clothes off, I will be serving tea in five minutes, chop chop.'

After tea Mum sent Rebecca a text to see if it was convenient to telephone her. Rebecca text back straight away so Mum rang her. After they had said hello and Mum had checked how Rebecca was, Mum passed me the phone saying to Rebecca, 'Titch has got some news for you.'

I was so excited, 'Rebecca, it's me, we're going to Granny's for Christmas, Mum has just told me and Daniel and I'm going to be in the school play. Are you coming home really soon?'

Rebecca laughed, 'Titch, slow down, I didn't get a word of that, what did you say about Granny's?'

'We are going to Granny's for Christmas and I'm in the school play, Mrs Rigsby told me this morning.'

'Wow that is great, listen, I'm struggling to hear you, put Mum back on the phone please.'

So I passed the phone back and heard Mum saying that yes it was true, we were going to Granny's for Christmas and that I had a starring role in the Christmas concert at school. I then heard her saying something about what date Rebecca was coming home and whether she'd sorted the train times out.

I really did think I was going to burst; Rebecca was talking about coming home soon, we were off to see

Granny and I was in the school concert. How exciting was all that?

When Mum had finished speaking to Rebecca I spoke again and told her that I loved her and that I was missing her. Rebecca told me that she was missing me as well but that she would be home soon and we would have a lovely time together. We said good-bye then it was Dad's turn to talk to her so I went upstairs to write an important letter. I started writing it but then didn't know what to say. There were lots of toys, games and books I wanted but I knew that there was only one thing that I really wanted for Christmas and I wasn't sure whether Father Christmas could manage that. Suddenly I felt cross with him.

Dear Father Christmas,

I have been a good girl all year and have not been ~~nastie~~ nasty to my big sister and brother. But my Mummy is poorly and it isn't fair because she is nice and is not mean to people. Can you make her better please and make that ~~horible~~ horrible thing go away. When you come to see us we won't be at our house we will be at grannys so will you leave the presents there. Daddy will leave you a glass of sherry and some mince pies for the raindeer.

Thank you love Kitty

I decided I mustn't say nasty things to Father Christmas even though I thought them. I hoped he would understand. When I went back downstairs, Mum was speaking to Granny on the telephone. When she had finished speaking she let me talk to Granny. I told her my news about school and she said it was brilliant and that I was brilliant.

Mum took me to bed when it was bedtime and as she tucked me in she put Tootles by my side and told me to tell her all about my exciting day. But I think I was so tired I didn't have time to tell her everything before I fell asleep.

TWENTY SIX

Angela

As usual, despite all my planning the morning of our departure to Mum's was spent doing last minute packing and trying to organise everybody. Nathan was in charge of packing the car; he had a really good system for managing to cram everything into the boot with military precision. He commandeered Daniel to be his assistant, which mainly entailed carrying all the bags to the car and then standing back while Nathan took over. I watched Daniel helping his Dad; they were laughing and joking with each other. It was good to take a few minutes to just stand and watch them getting on so well. I suppose just as my relationship with Rebecca had altered over the year so had Nathan and Daniel's.

Rebecca was bustling around in the kitchen helping me to get organised. She had been home nearly a week and had quickly settled back into family life. It was good to have her back home, it was only when she was home that I realised how much I missed her when she was away. The house seemed empty without her. However, I wasn't thinking that when she came home with what seemed to be a terms worth of washing.

Titch was so excited I was concerned she was going to burst. Rebecca and I tried to calm her down but our attempts were in vain. Our trip to Mum's seemed to be the catalyst for lifting all the worries that had been ever present for her for the last year. As I watched her running round the house saying her goodbyes to all her toys and belongings I realised that all year there has been a shadow hanging over her. At times it had been more noticeable than others but nevertheless it had been there, in some form constantly. But today as she was bouncing with excitement it had gone. Once again I wondered how such a young child could be so affected by the illness when we had tried our best to shield her from it. I looked at her and wondered how long it would be before she was again weighted down with worries because of IT.

After much activity the car was packed, all the children were sorted and we were ready to head south to Mum's. I thought back to our journey to Mum's the previous year. There had been so much excitement from the back of the car but hard as I tried I struggled to join in with the anticipation. Although there was no official medical news then to confirm my worries I was pretty sure that there was something wrong with my health. I didn't know what of course, but I knew that something was not right. Much as I tried to not let it spoil the holiday for everyone, I was aware that the worries were regularly taking over my conscious thoughts.

Thinking back about the year, we had been on one heck of a roller-coaster. The appearance of IT in our family had altered everything and had tested us to the limits but also we had grown from it. I wish it had never bothered us but in some respects we had adjusted well and had grown to live with it. I probably wouldn't have been thinking that if it hadn't been for the appointment with the young GP last month. Her consultation had really helped me think about things differently. She had helped me to see that IT was not just affecting me physically but all aspects of my life and my family's too.

We were all a year older but also each one of us had changed and grown older too. All three children had a sense of maturity that they didn't have prior to the diagnosis. This was most keenly seen in Rebecca; she was now a young woman, any traces of a teenager having gone. Maybe she would have matured anyway because of being away at university. She had taken on so many new roles during the past year. From what we could gather she was loving her new job and had made some good friends through it. She was also settling into academic life and was now enjoying her studies and doing really well. I'm sure it must have been very hard at times to focus on her studies when she had been worrying about me and home. But to her credit she had found the strength and tenacity to work hard and get some good grades in her assignments.

Equally Daniel and Titch had done some serious growing up during the previous twelve months. They had been robbed of some of the innocence associated with childhood. Their protected, safe worlds being just not quite as safe or protected anymore. They had both dealt with IT in their own ways. I wished I had been more prepared to support them, I wished I had been given information from a professional about what they might be feeling, how they might react and how best to support them. But we didn't get any offer of help and so just had to struggle on trying our best and fumbling our way through.

I'd been blessed to have some great support from friends and family. I didn't know what I would have done if it hadn't been for Elspeth and Tracey. They had been there every time I had needed a bit extra support. Both, in their own ways had been true friends and I owed them so much. They had both come for coffee a few days before we left for Mum's. They were busy of course with preparing for Christmas but it was good to see them briefly. Tracey alluded to some new work she was planning for the coming year. She didn't say much more but when she mentioned it to Elspeth there was a knowing look shared between them which told me that Tracey was planning something. I suspected it might have had something to do with the conversation we had had when I was telling her about the consultation with the GP. Thinking back to when I told her about that I remembered seeing her mind plotting something. All she said, once she had sown the seeds was that all would be revealed in early January.

And what about Nathan and Mum. What would I have done without them this year? Nathan had been amazing; without his support I knew I would not have been able to carry on. During the darkest hours of all this it had been Nathan who had been by my side, who had held me close and kept me going. We'd had our rough times too; there had been more arguments than ever before and at times I had been really quite awful to him. I went through a particularly bleak period where I felt I had lost my looks and my femininity. I couldn't cope with Nathan showing me any affection because I felt that I didn't deserve it. I knew I was blocking him out and inadvertently pushing him away. I didn't want him to be physically or emotionally close to me. It was almost as if I was rejecting his love. Maybe I had some ridiculous idea that by rejecting him then I was lessening the blow for when I died. Was I preparing him for life without me? I glanced over to him; he looked older, his thick mass of hair looked greyer and he didn't have the dark skin tone that represented being out in all weathers working. How could I even contemplate leaving him, not now and not in the future? Again I resolved to fight IT as much as I could.

I was brought out of my reflections by Titch.

'Mum I need the toilet.'

I looked again to Nathan 'not long now to our coffee stop, do you think you can wait five minutes?'

'I'll try.'

Thankfully we were very close to the café where we usually stopped for a break. Nathan found a table and skilfully managed to squeeze another chair in to the space so we could all sit together. I made a dash for the Ladies with Titch. After our drinks we had a quick look round the shop part of the café before heading on our way. I telephoned Mum to let her know where we were so she could estimate our time of arrival. I assured her we would be there for lunch but that it might have to be a late one.

We shoehorned the children back into the rear of the car with the usual moans and grumbles as they jostled for the maximum space they could. Rebecca and Daniel sat by the doors and Titch was squeezed in between them. Not for the first time I wondered how much longer we would be able to manage with our old car. The children were growing so fast the back seat really wasn't comfortable for them.

The three of them were having a conversation about pantomimes. Titch was trying to remember the one that we had taken them to. She must have only been about three and had not really enjoyed it. As I recalled she was scared of the Wicked Stepmother and cried every time she was on stage. The other two had tormented her relentlessly for ages after. Nathan and I listened to their conversation and how each of them had different memories from the performance.

I too started to think back about the pantomimes I had been to. As a child, our annual treat was to go to the pantomime. My favourite was Dick Whittington, I loved the idea of a boy having such a close relationship with his cat and how he metamorphosed from living in poverty to having so much money and power. I thought again how the traditional stories used in pantomimes always told of good beating evil and there always being a happy ending. My formative years had been shaped with the idea that whatever difficulties stood in your way you could overcome them and triumph in the end. This year I'd constantly had people shouting to me 'IT's behind you' and I'd been constantly trying to overcome evil. I shuddered to myself, would our family's pantomime have a happy ending? I wasn't sure it would but what I was sure of was that I was going to try my hardest for us all to have the best, happiest Christmas ever.

'Can you see the sea yet?' I asked as we got closer to Mum's.

'I can' shouted Titch with great enthusiasm.

'No you can't Liar Liar' said Daniel as he pushed an elbow in her side.

'Ouch, yes I can then, I can see it in my mind.'

Nathan quickly intervened, 'not much further and we will all be able to see it. What do you think Granny will have made for lunch?'

The children tried to guess what we would be having. The favourite answer was soup. I suspected that they would be right with that. One of Mum's staple recipes was her leek and potato soup and home-made crusty rolls.

'Do you think there might be some mince pies too?' asked Nathan. He loved Mum's mince pies and always managed to eat far more than was perhaps good for him.

'All this talk of food is making me hungry' I said as I stretched my legs into the foot well of the car. 'I hope Granny has got that kettle on.'

With the talk of food, Daniel and Titch had forgotten their squabble and peace had been regained in the back seat.

'Did anyone remember to tell Father Christmas that we would be here and not at home?' asked Nathan.

'I sent him a text' said Rebecca joining in the pretence for Titch's sake 'he didn't text back but I guess he is a bit busy at the moment.'

I wasn't sure how much Titch really still believed in Father Christmas and how many more years it would be before the whole idea of him was too babyish for her maturing years. But for now it was lovely that she still held on to the idea of him. So not all her innocence had been stripped away I thought to myself as we headed down the hill into the village where I knew there would be a roaring log fire and a massive big hug waiting for me.

TWENTY SEVEN

Rebecca

I turned and gave Granny one more wave before the car turned the corner. She was standing in the middle of the road waving. I knew she was crying. She looked smaller and older than she ever had done before, a crumpled shell of the strong woman that I knew and loved. She always cried when we left her, but this time it was very different. Everything was all very different and nothing would be the same again.

Hello,

I hope you have enjoyed reading the story of the Williamson's family on their journey through a life-limiting illness.

The writing of Our Family and IT was influenced by the work I have been involved in for some years. I have worked with children and families in different settings for many years, latterly as the manager of a Barnardo's family support service. It was while at Barnardo's that I became interested in dying, death, bereavement and family life. My PhD researched children's lives when a parent is at the end of life.

My research and subsequent work have been a driving force for the book. Since completing my PhD (2010) I have been working hard to get children and parental life-limiting illness on the agenda. The idea of writing about the problem in the form of a novel was seen as being another vehicle for bringing it to a wider audience.

My hope is that while enjoying the book and, hopefully, becoming 'lost' in a good story, the changes and challenges that Angela and her family face will prompt the reader to briefly stop and question why the family is exposed to some of the issues they have to manage. I believe that if Angela had received more social and emotional support from the point of diagnosis some of the problems she and her family faced would not have occurred.

I deliberately chose to be unspecific about IT. I didn't want to focus on one illness at the detriment to others, recognising that the diagnosis of any life-limiting illnesses can be catastrophic to the patient and their family.

While all the characters in the book are fictional they represent families throughout the United Kingdom (and beyond) who are trying to cope with a physical illness that might not be curable. The events in the book are all fictitious but are based on real life stories that I have heard during my research and practice. All the emotions, behaviours and incidents with the family are plausible and I am sure that families who are living with IT can identify with some of the chapters.

I carefully selected the ages of the children to capture how children at different ages are likely to cope and manage (or not manage as is sadly sometimes the case) with all the changes and challenges that life-limiting illness brings to family life. Their reactions and behaviour are based on research about how children at certain ages and stages are likely to react.

Within the book there are some key points that I hope have been highlighted within the text. For example, in Chapter Fourteen, when Daniel is struggling with all that is happening around him he recalls a conversation he had with Nathan – 'He told me that, at that time, the treatment wasn't working as much as they had hoped. But he didn't say anymore, instead he told me not to worry as it would all be okay.' This is important because Nathan refers to those responsible for Angela's care as 'they'. However, it is helpful for children and

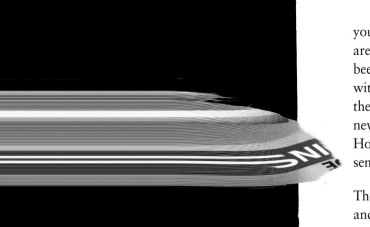

young people to know who 'they' are. For Daniel 'they' are nameless, invisible people. Here it would have been good for Daniel if 'they' had become real people with names and roles so that he could begin to 'know' them. It might be that the children and young people never actually meet the people caring for their parent. However, just having a name provides them with a sense of being involved.

The notion of being involved to the extent that children and young people want to be is really important. As we have seen throughout the book, all three children wanted and tried to be involved in what was happening but at times were pushed away by Angela and Nathan. This behaviour from parents is often used to help protect their children from all the awful things that are happening but sometimes it has a negative effect. For a long time I have held the belief that parenting is the hardest job in the world and I know from research and a dash of common sense that having to tell your children you are ill with an illness that might not be curable must be the hardest conversation you will ever have. However, it is also an important one that can make such a difference to the children's lives.

If I needed to pick out the top ten points from this book they would be –

1. Children's behaviour can change in different ways when trying to manage the situation.

2. Children at different ages will react differently – no two children are the same and one size definitely does not fit all.

3. There is a role for professionals to help give social and emotional support.

4. There are times when 'normal' family life continues.

5. Children will know that something is happening in their family – if they are not given some information they will put two and two together but not come up with four as their answer.

6. Having an emergency plan in place could be a really helpful strategy. Just like Angela it is not something ill parents might want to contemplate but in the case of an emergency it could be invaluable for the children, the person caring for them and the parent.

7. The diagnosis of a potentially life-limiting illness affects everyone in the family not just the person with the diagnosis.

8. Making time to actually listen to children and to actually hear what they are saying is imperative.

9. Asking for support is not a sign of weakness nor is showing emotions (even in the rugby club!).

10. We can make a difference to children's lives – please help me to make a difference.

This book has not been written as a 'self-help' style book and I am not offering advice or suggestions about how families should manage life-limiting illness. But what I would like is for people to begin to engage in a debate about this important issue. We know that life-limiting illness is not prejudiced and will (and does) affect people from all sections of society. However, while there are examples of great practice out there where the patient is not seen in isolation and is offered holistic care (including support for their children), this is the exception and not the rule. I feel passionately that there is a lot more that could and should be done to support this community of children and their families. If you too feel that this issue cannot be ignored for any longer please head to my website and make contact.

Thank you,

Rachel

April 2018

www.rachelfearnley.co.uk